CONTENTS

C000256061

Prologue

Chapter One – Planning..1

Chapter Two – Europe..13

Chapter Three – Into Asia Minor....................................25

Chapter Four – The Holy Land.......................................39

Chapter Five – Jordan and Lebanon 53

Chapter Six – Egypt 64

Chapter Seven – The Mokoto 79

Chapter Eight – Kenya 86

Chapter Nine – Tanganyika...99

Chapter Ten – Rhodesia..112

Chapter Eleven – South Africa......................................125

Chapter Twelve – Basutoland to Ghana 135

Chapter Thirteen – Nigeria...146

Chapter Fourteen – Homewards 157

Epilogue..166

To Travel Hopefully

The aircraft disappeared over the palm trees, leaving a burning building and a few bodies. Suddenly all was quiet, save for the distant tapping of small-arms fire. Soldiers in ragged uniforms emerged from cover. When a hospital is bombed, at least there isn't far to drag the wounded. The magpie snicker of a machine gun sounded from down the road. The soldiers clambered into and onto anything left with wheels, and the motley caravan moved off towards the East and the border with the Cameroons.

"Why does the Federal lot have to bomb a hospital?" demanded a doctor in a strong Yorkshire accent, as he bandaged a groaning nurse.

"Why did the Biafrans have to shelter here?" responded his colleague, swabbing down a bloody table. "And I see they've taken Charlie with them."

"Charlie?"

"Our Land Rover. The lads who brought it out from England - before you came - called it that."

Chapter One - Planning

The River Cam flowed slowly under the bridge of white stone. Along the white stone rails were rows of white stone spheres, the size of footballs. A mason with a sense of humour had cut an arc out of one sphere, like an orange with a segment missing. This was mounted among its fellows with the gap facing the river. The only ways of discovering the incomplete orb were to peer from a boat below or, standing on the bridge, to feel round the back of each one. The latter course was taken by dozens of tourists who had read of the anomaly in a guide book.

One Summer Sunday a small man with spectacles had positioned his deck-chair at the edge of the college lawn, and was watching the bridge above through eyes half-closed against the sun. It was his wont to invite a few of his pupils to "take a dish of tea on the Sabbath", and half a dozen undergraduates were spread on the grass round about, respectfully listening to the great man. They might affectionately call him "Charlie" behind his back, but always "Sir" to his face.

"The reason why there are relatively few Catholics in East Anglia," he was saying, "is because the land is flat." He stopped to squint intently at the bridge. There was a long pause.

Andrew fidgeted uncomfortably. He knew that the Professor of Comparative Religion was waiting for someone to take the bait, and that everyone else was waiting for someone else to take it. How difficult it was to endure silence. He sighed. The distant traffic muttered from across the meadowland. "How does that follow?" asked Andrew.

"Perfectly simple," smiled the P. of C.R., "flat country, no railway tunnels; no tunnels, no Irish navvies; no Irish, no accompanying priests; no priests, no spread of Catholicism."

"Of course," murmured Andrew.

"They tell me you are off to Africa," said the P. of C.R.

"Only for a couple of months, and not until next year. We're delivering a Land Rover to a mission hospital in Nigeria. Jim is coming too, and another couple of chaps from Emmanuel."

"I'm glad you'll have Jim to look after you," nodded the old man, "he'll get you back in one piece. I don't suppose you have room for another? I would make a good cook - No, don't laugh, I've always wanted to do something worthwhile, instead of teaching you lot. Who will be doing the cooking, incidentally?"

"All four of us," Jim put in. He was a couple of years older and a couple of stones heavier than Andrew. "It's going to be an awfully democratic expedition."

The Professor frowned. "I fear that democracy rarely works in practice...." He broke off suddenly. A chorus of middle-aged American accents came from the bridge:

"Hey, this must be the bridge with the missing wedge."

"They all look the same to me."

"George, Honey, find it for me, Sweetie," pouted a female voice. The Prof. of C.R. leaned forward in his deck chair, tea-cup shaking slightly, spectacles glinting. Andrew couldn't help thinking of a praying-mantis poised to strike.

"Can you feel round the back, George?" asked the female voice.

"Yep, this one seems to have a gap, and I can feel - Oh shit!"

"George, what is it?"

"All over my hand.....Hell! It looks like marmalade! How would that get there?"

On the lawn below, the small man with spectacles was writhing silently, tears pouring down his face.

"Surely," whispered Andrew to Jim, "surely Charlie didn't....?"

Jim nodded. "I don't think he likes tourists," he murmured.

"How about 'from Emma to Enugu'?" asked David, his mouth full of toast. Richard brushed crumbs from his shoulder and bent over the map.

"Where's Enugu?" he asked.

"Eastern Nigeria. Left of Cameroon. It's fairly close to Ituk Mban."

"A what?"

"It's pronounced 'a tomb bang' - the hospital place where we're leaving the Land Rover. But you can't have an embossed heading for the begging letters saying 'from Emma to Ituk Mban' - no alliteration, no oomph, won't grab the attention. More toast?"

"No thanks. Must go. Due on the river." Richard rowed for the College First Boat. He also had the job of coaching the College Sixth Boat, in which the novices like David, Jim and Andrew, floundered.

David went back to the map on the floor. The AA gave a choice of two routes across the Sahara, the Tanezrouft and the Hoggar, both starting from Algeria and reaching Kano in Northern Nigeria three thousand miles later. Half of the distance was desert. The AA advised them to carry enough drinking water for a gallon per person per day. Andrew had remarked that they would spend the entire day either drinking or piddling; but someone assured him that you never needed to relieve yourself in the Sahara since there would be only steam and the odd crystal.

The AA also recommended carrying enough distilled water to allow for two pints a week evaporating from the battery. Richard had remarked that this was rather obvious. The others, to whom the thought would never have occurred, were much impressed, and had there and then appointed him Expedition Mechanic. He insisted that such an honour should be matched by titles of comparable grandeur for the others. So Andrew, who had studied Hebrew and had once spent a month in France, was appointed Interpreter. Nobody could think of suitable jobs for Jim or David. Andrew had kindly said that their abilities were of a more general nature; and Jim had explained to David that this meant they would get the jobs nobody else wanted.

The Automobile Association Notes contained many helpful hints on Saharan travel, such as 'it is customary to stop and greet fellow travellers (this information is based on reports from returning members)'; Andrew had wondered what proportion of members returned. Other helpful advice was that 'it is extremely inadvisable to travel between May and September' - which, of course, was the time when they would be going.

Andrew's room was one of the biggest and oldest in the College. It was greatly admired, not for these qualities, but because it had an open fire. Strictly speaking, there was no need for a fire on an early May evening, but ambience was important. Round the smouldering coals (well, you couldn't expect a chimney of such vintage to have a good draught) people were drinking coffee. Brian, a likeable hedonist, was contemplating a career in management, having recently been accepted as a trainee by a manufacturer of tobacco products.

"It's not everyone's idea of glamour, selling cigarettes," he was saying, "particularly if you're as talented as I am. But it was that or the church; and although I quite fancy the thought of being a bishop - the uniform is attractive - the religious part would be terribly trying. So cigarettes it is. And you needn't look superior, Richard! A career as a senior executive is better than wasting one's life teaching, even if it does give you an excuse to spend an extra year doing a Dip. Ed. instead of working."

Richard was not easily provoked. "Yes," he smiled, "I'm looking forward to it. And I'm sure you'll make a great executive. Now, push off - we've got to sort out this expedition."

"Oh yes," groaned Brian, "the Great Expedition! I can't understand why you want to go - bound to be uncomfortable. Sort of ego trip if you ask me - 'look at us getting bitten by things to bring civilisation to Africa.'. Personally, if I wanted to help the natives, I wouldn't send two theologians, a classicist and a psychologist." He laughed , picked up his scarf, and left, still chuckling.

"He has got a point," muttered Andrew, frowning. "How on earth are we going to persuade the University Expeditions Board to give their official blessing?"

This formal approval was important. Firms had got fed up with requests for sponsorship from dozens of aspiring explorers every year, so had agreed to support a limited number of expeditions approved by the university. But to get this approval was not easy. Successful applicants tended to be archaeologists on Mesopotamian digs, or mountaineers attempting unclimbed peaks in Bhutan. Just delivering a Land Rover would not be enough.

"Couldn't we go without official approval?" David wondered aloud.

"Makes it much more expensive," said Jim, "and second-class somehow. We want something special, not an amateur picnic."

"How about taking in Ethiopia - it sounds expedition-worthy; or doing something on the Coptic Church?" asked Andrew.

"Doing what on the Coptic Church?" sighed Richard

There was a sizeable silence.

"Right," said Jim, "we have until December to come up with an objective to impress the Expeditions Board. We'll have to have a deadline meeting in November, yes? And I don't know about you, but in two weeks time I've got exams, so let's forget Africa until afterwards."

Exams came and went. The sun shone and the Cam echoed to the traditional hearty encouragement for college oarsmen competing in the "May Bumps" (which took place in June). Everyone in Third Year exchanged printed invitation cards to each other's farewell parties. Underlying the surface noise and jollity there was a sense of anticlimax. Most exam results had been satisfactory; the weather was dreamy; the remaining few days of term would be full of degree ceremonies and formal dinners among the college silver; but a sort of empty feeling lurked nearby. Andrew, who might have been a poet had he got round to it, said that they were mourning their departure from Elysian fields. Richard explained to David, a mere scientist, that Elysian fields were the Greek equivalent of heaven.

While they were exchanging such deep philosophies by the college pond in that mellow time that June arranges after lunch, Jim arrived with a small fair thing in his wake and introduced them to Sally. David kissed her hand - he felt safe with other people's girlfriends. Richard told her she was a great improvement on the ones that normally swarmed round Jim, and Andrew asked Sally whether she had always been attracted to older men.

"These are the other three-quarters of the Great Expedition," sighed Jim apologetically. "Can you imagine being imprisoned for weeks in a small tin van with this lot?" The other three quarters suggested Sal might like to join them in Jim's place, but Jim said that he couldn't allow her to spend months with snakes and irritating insects - even if they did come from Emmanuel.

All too soon frivolity had to give way, and dull reality pulled the wings off the butterfly years. David found post-graduate Sheffield a rude awakening. The smoke rolling up from the Rotherham valley was different from mist drifting over the Cam. His research topic was

Programmed Instruction. It was based on the work of an American Psychologist who had taught pigeons to do complicated tasks by breaking them down into simple components, rewarding the pigeons with food for performing each of these bits, then making the reward conditional on joining two bits, and so on until a complex sequence of behaviour, like pecking a table-tennis ball over a net, had been learned. This basic idea had been extended to human learning, and it was found that school subjects like maths could be successfully taught by breaking a topic into simple logical steps, explaining each step and getting the student to answer simple questions on each step (the reward being the satisfaction of getting the answer right), until the whole topic had been mastered. Indeed, the sceptics argued, good teachers had done this anyway from time dot.

Programmed Instruction could be incorporated in book form or in more sophisticated machines, and could, in theory, teach without human intervention. UNESCO became interested in it as a means of overcoming teacher shortages in developing countries. Sergei Something, a Russian gentleman who headed the UNESCO Educational Department in Paris, chanced to visit the Sheffield Psychology Department, and David asked him, rather tentatively, whether UNESCO might sponsor a survey of new teaching methods in Africa. To his surprise, Comrade Sergei became quite animated, and said that it was an excellent idea - not that they could fund anything expensive of course, but a modest project would have the full support of his organisation. David said that he might be able to come up with something, provided that three other people agreed.

They met in Cambridge that November, where Jim was doing his final year. Being one of the last age-group to have done National Service (in a tank on the Rhine) he had come to Emmanuel after the younger three. The others welcomed an excuse to return without actually admitting that they missed the place. They had agreed that Programmed Instruction, whatever it was, might impress a University Expeditions Committee, and now they were focusing on routes. Jim's floor was covered in maps.

"We should really sample East, South and West Africa," David was saying, "but how much time will we have?" Not much, was the answer. Exams meant they couldn't leave before the end of June, and

Jim and Andrew had to be back in late September. They decided that they could manage a country a week if the four of them split up each day and visited a representative sample of schools, taking questionnaires about the local situation for teachers to complete. But which countries could they reach in the time?

"Personally, I don't mind, so long as you include Northern Rhodesia," said Richard. "I've just got a job there for September, so you can drop me off!"

"Hey, we could go through Ethiopia!" Andrew was warming to the idea. They bent over the maps. Europe had good roads, and getting round the end of the Mediterranean didn't look a problem. Egypt seemed to have all-weather roads to Aswan. Then they would have to get through Sudan.

"That's where the problems start," Richard mused. "According to the AA the road South as far as Khartoum is 'not negotiable between June and November because of excessive heat', but maybe they're over-cautious and we'll be OK if we get there by mid-July."

"Then we cut across to Ethiopia, and Bob's your uncle - plain sailing down through East Africa on tarmac!" cut in Andrew.

"Sure?" The others sounded doubtful.

"Well, we've got a few months to investigate," said Richard, "and since I'm in London, I'll go round the embassies and ask about the roads."

"Good," said Jim, "I'll put that route into the Expeditions Board application, but I'll need more information on this Programmed Instruction thing. And, what are we calling ourselves?" Routes, finance, timing were minor problems compared to this. At least four titles were suggested, and protracted negotiations ensued. "Applications of Educational Technology South of the Sahara" was felt to be too weighty; "Let's Go with UNESCO!" was too frivolous; and "Into Africa" was thought to be too theatrical for their serious purpose. They finally settled on something solid and business-like.

"Cambridge to Capetown 1964" achieved official university approval in January, and they started planning in earnest. To say that a well-oiled machine swung into operation would be overdoing it, but certainly there was a great deal of activity, more or less co-ordinated at times. Richard and David went to the Rover works at Solihull for a week's basic course on Taking Land Rovers to Pieces, which they achieved quite well, and Putting Them Back Together, which was more difficult. Andrew, who had added Route-planning to his Translation duties, discovered that you couldn't go through Israel. Into, yes; but the Arab country on the other side wouldn't let you out again. They looked for a sea alternative from Lebanon to Egypt. Jim had mumps, and the others avoided him, self-preservation overcoming compassion.

In February a letter arrived from the Sudanese Department of Tourism:

"Dear and kind Sirs, We are delighted to hear of your plans to visit our beautiful country, thus strengthening the bonds of mutual respect and affection which exist between our peoples. We know that you will greatly enjoy your time with us and admire the facilities available on either hand. We look forward to welcoming you personally to our great nation. Noting with respect that you will be journeying in July we would point out that the Southern part of your route will be closed due to floods. The other part may be attempted in convoys of more than one vehicle. Again may we express our joy at your visit and wish you a memorable occasion.

Yours etc.

P.S. Due to the present revolution all road transport has been banned.

In March a shipping agent in London said he could find them a passage down the Red Sea to avoid Sudan. They could apparently join a ship at Beirut that would take them via the Suez Canal to Massawa in Eritrea. The AA's 'Trans Africa Highways' listed Massawa as "the main port of Ethiopia" with all-weather road to Addis Ababa, adding "police and malaria prevalent". It looked good.

Now that the route was settled they could concentrate on everything else. Andrew was arranging financial resources at various banks along the route, which would also hold any mail for them. Jim went to lectures on tropical health, and informed the others that the most important thing when bitten by a snake was to take the snake with you to the nearest hospital - whether for identification or treatment of the snake was unclear.

April. The Bugle Horn was somewhere between Oxford, Cambridge, Sheffield and London. Actually, it was closer to Oxford, where Andrew was doing his pre-vicarage course, and had been chosen for one of their periodic Final Planning Conferences on Andrew's recommendation. He said that the steaks there really should be experienced - "before the months of hardship to come."

The Land Rover had been delivered and they spent the morning admiring it. It was a long-wheel-base model, with an extra door at the back. April sunshine gleamed on the grey body and cream hard-top. They took turns to drive slowly round the car-park in low range four-wheel drive and try out the winch mounted over the front bumper.

"You tie a rope to a nearby tree, wrap it twice round the winch and pull yourself out of whatever you're in," explained Richard.

"What if there isn't a tree?" asked Andrew, and was ignored.

With transparent kindergarten joy they stroked the two spare heavy-duty tyres on back-door and bonnet, and smelled the petrolly smell when you switched to auxiliary fuel tank. Twenty-nine gallons capacity was thought likely to cover any gaps between petrol stations. The one disappointment was the horn. "You can't have a hulking brute like this emitting a weak asthmatic bleat in moments of emergency!" protested Jim. But, apart from that, the bonding went well, and the Expedition and Charlie decided they liked each other immensely. The Land Rover had been named Charlie after the Professor of Comparative Religion, to symbolise cheerfulness and reliability.

The afternoon was more tedious - routes and schedules and visas and contacts and budgets. Jim was concerned at the sheer volume of stores accumulating from donor firms, and expressed a wish to be able to close the door of his room again. This would involve someone removing a dozen jars of marmalade (Cooper's thick peel), twenty-four tins of cheese, twenty-four tins of Ostamilk, eighty-four packets of dehydrated soup, sugar (seventy pounds), toilet paper (six furlongs of) and a pressure cooker. Andrew nobly volunteered his parents' house at Aylesbury as a depository, and David, blushing slightly, said that he had been invited to a Ball at Homerton College the next week, so he could collect the stuff. Richard enquired whether the strapping wench who used to beat them at tennis came from Homerton, and violence threatened to disrupt the day. But the others intervened and work resumed.

"Right," summarised Jim some hours later," we start on schools in Addis Ababa at the end of July, move down East Africa, drop Richard off in Northern Rhodesia, and finish South African schools by the end of September when Andrew and I have to fly home. The only way to manage West Africa is for poor David to do Nigeria and Ghana on his own, so he and Charlie ship from Capetown to Lagos in October. For some reason David's Prof. doesn't mind him being away for so long! Anyhow, when he has finished, Charlie can finally be delivered to the Ituk Mban Mission. They and the donor have agreed to the revised schedule, thank goodness. Now, what's left to do?"

"I need your signatures on the Bulgarian permits," said Richard, "and we may have to get additional insurance for Charlie at the border, but it is a quicker route, and the visas are only seven shillings."

"I'm getting quotes on the Capetown to Lagos leg," said Andrew. "Luckily there seem quite a few shipping companies doing that route. Now, anyone ready for a drink?"

"Oh, that reminds me," put in Jim, "we got two cases of sherry from Harvey's!" (Murmurs of approval) "But I sold them and bought the camp beds. Never mind, we have the offer of two thousand cigarettes if we collect them in Beirut - tax reason or something. Anyone smoke?" David appeared to be the only practitioner.

They did justice to the Bugle Horn steaks and wended their various ways into the gathering smog. What a relief to have everything organised at last.

The next week the shipping agent phoned. There was no ship from Beirut to Massawa in July. Their hearts fell. But he thought there were ships from Aqaba to Massawa, by-passing Lebanon and Egypt as well as Sudan. Their hearts rose - this short-cut would save weeks.

May. Jim was paid a fee of five guineas by Anglian TV for an interview about the Expedition. Richard and David were asked to appear on BBC - and fell over themselves accepting. They were less euphoric when they found that forty-seven other expeditions were appearing on the same BBC 2 programme, and that it was broadcast only in the London area. The final insult was to be featured between an adolescent hitch-hiking to Greece and a girls' hockey tour from a Technical College ("not that there's anything wrong with Techs.," said Richard "or girls for that matter; but really!"). There was no news yet of the Aqaba-Massawa boat, but school visits had to be finalised, and the soft-hearted secretaries at the Sheffield Psychology Department squeezed into their work-load a few letters a day to Africa. Meanwhile, a quiet Manxman called Felix fitted the Land Rover with a glorious klaxon which emitted full-throated roars worthy of Charlie's dignity. A letter arrived from the Nigerian Embassy, asking for import duty on a Land Rover - it was to be the start of protracted negotiations.

June. There was still no news of the Aqaba-Massawa boat. Anxiety levels rose, for the schedule of visits to schools and educationalists assumed that they would reach Ethiopia by the end of July. Bureaucracy increased the stress levels: Syria, for example, wanted evidence of a permit to enter Jordan before issuing a visa; Jordan wanted evidence they had a boat ticket from Aqaba before issuing an entry permit - difficult if you hadn't found a boat. Nigeria was still demanding advance payment of import duties; David referred them to the Commonwealth Agreement on Charitable Purposes. ("Does it exist?" asked Richard. "It sounds like it should if it doesn't," said David.)

The last weekend in June saw frenetic activity at an Aylesbury Vicarage. Richard was still taking exams in London, but the others were trying to fit three months' food into the back of Charlie. Since their schedule allowed no time for illness, they had decided to avoid local food, living exclusively off the donated rations.
"Do we need forty-eight tins of condensed milk?"
"It's for the twenty-four packets of porridge."
"But I don't like porridge."

"Try forty-eight tins of condensed milk without it, and you will."

"What's this Horlicks Dehydrated Meat Bar?"

"Ah, that's a special treat - to be kept for an auspicious occasion."

"No, no, no, the medical chest must be accessible."

"Couldn't we jettison half the soap?"

The 'phone rang. Maybe it would be news of the boat from Aqaba. Andrew returned in a sort of daze.

"It's Richard," he said. "The Kenya High Commission says we can't go through their Northern territory - unrest in the Somali border area or something. And that's the only way South from Ethiopia."

It was Friday. They were due to leave Dover on the next Wednesday. They 'phoned the shipping agent, who said he would try to find something to get them from the Middle East direct to Mombasa, but that Rome was not built in a day. They told him he could have four days. He said he couldn't do it. They said they would just have to leave him to find what he could, and forward any news to them en route. He muttered that they might just have to try to find something themselves when they got to Jordan.

It was not a serenely confident Expedition that prepared for embarkation.

Chapter Two - Europe

July 1st. 1964 brought a bright and windy morning to Dover. David, a poor sailor, regarded the choppy sea anxiously.

"You can't be seasick," Richard assured him, "You live on a small island in the Irish Sea!"

"Yes, plenty of practice at being seasick."

"Tickets, Andrew?" asked Jim.

"I'm looking after routes, not tickets. Oh, are these the ones?"

Jim sighed to himself and wondered how they would ever get to Africa.

They watched England diminishing in the distance. Someone should say something memorable, they thought, to be recorded for posterity. But no one did. They stood on the deck in silence, thinking their own thoughts. Jim thought about Sally; they had been engaged a week now. The others had been loudly congratulatory, but he suspected they feared he would be a pale and sadly loitering weight on the Expedition, pining the weeks away. Richard thought what a rather splendid place England was, and wondered if signing on for three years in Northern Rhodesia had been such a good idea. Andrew was hoping that his aunt, with whom they had stayed the previous night in Kent, wouldn't tell his parents that they had slept on the front room floor. The Expedition's PR image was important, but it had rained, and the tents would have got wet. David thought that he wouldn't be seasick after all.

How they got into the middle of Brussels, which they were supposed to have by-passed, nobody was sure. Maybe it was because Brussels had evolved a fascinating one-way system that funnelled you exactly where you didn't want to go.

"Which road, Navigator?" asked David in a higher-pitched voice than usual, wondering on which side of the trams to drive.

"I'm in the back," came a muffled backish sort of voice from Andrew. "Ask whoever's got the map." The Land Rover had three seats in front, and the fourth body had to squeeze on top of the boxes in the back. Actually it was quite comfortable if you re-arranged the softer items, but the lack of side-windows made it better for sleeping than sightseeing. If you bent your head against the roof, though, you could see out of the rear window ("Why are those policemen waving?"). The middle seat in front was the worst position - made you realise how many elbows were attached to a human body.

They were near a small town called Louvain when they stopped at seven that evening. Jim, driving, had spotted a cherry orchard which looked inviting. Andrew, official linguist, was called on to negotiate.

"Do they speak Walloon or Flem?" he whispered. It didn't matter much since he spoke neither. Entente was achieved by shouting slowly in English, and they self-consciously set about pitching tents and cooking. Supper started, as it would for months, with rehydrated packet soup. That night it was an enjoyably new experience.

Now, interest in white-skinned campers might be expected in the Middle East or Africa, but why a large group of Belgians should gather to watch was surprising. Maybe it was the heavily-laden Land Rover, with its winch and extra spare tyres and petrol cans, that attracted them. The local lads challenged them to soccer after supper, cheered on by infants and grandmothers, and beat the Expedition, ten - seven. A perspiring Richard panted that they were right to decide to lose for the sake of international relations. Jim thought that the opposition goal-posts were closer together than their own.

The dew was falling as they spread their sleeping-bags beneath the cherry trees, and pumped up the petrol stove to make the Complan. There had been some protest at first over this geriatric brew, but Jim, in charge of health and welfare, had insisted. Next came the ablutions ritual - later in the journey standards would become more flexible, but tonight they washed their faces and brushed their teeth, in case anyone thought they didn't usually do so.

So here they were on foreign soil, at the portal of the unknown as Andrew put it. The months stretched uncertainly ahead of them - no problem with the route to Jordan, no qualms about Africa, once they got there, it was the bit between that was anxiously blank. But for now the air was sweet and grassy, the Complan tasted better than they had feared, and a sense of contentment percolated through the camp.

"Of course," said Richard, watching the stars, his head outside the tent, "it may not always be as easy as this."

The next morning they had finished their porridge and had packed up by eight. The cherry farmer and his family had assembled, presumably to wish them well on their awesome undertaking. There was much smiling and nodding, and a refusal to accept any payment. The expedition felt that some formal expression of gratitude was called for, so the Official Linguist was nudged forward:

"Peace be within your courts and plenteousness within your palaces!" said Andrew, shaking a sample of hands. Everyone smiled and nodded.

"Splendid grasp of European languages you have," murmured David as they headed for Liege and Koblenz. The concrete autobahns unwound smoothly beneath them for three hundred miles that day.

A detour to Heidelberg enabled them to visit an Emmanuel contemporary that evening. Duncan took them to a little restaurant on the banks of the Neckar - famed for its soup, he said. And it *was* good. After a third helping they enquired what it was. "Pig's blood and liver," the waiter proudly informed them, and they were very quiet for a time. An expensive and overcrowded camp site was found for the night - they decided that civilisation had its drawbacks, and imagined how much better the empty African plains would be.

Wednesday Belgium, Thursday Germany, Friday Austria, Saturday Yugoslavia . Already the details of previous days were blurring. Some particular scenes formed islands of memory in an ocean of jumbled landscapes: an eagle on a hay-rick, a pretty girl in Saltzburg who smiled and wished them "Gruss Gott", a jagged church steeple echoing the jagged peaks behind.

Each day seemed to end with a soccer fixture. No matter where they camped it was not long before a ball would appear accompanied by half a dozen local lads. They lost to Belgium, drew with Germany and beat Austria. After the crude nationalism of Wembley it was encouraging to find that sport was a language of friendship in village camp-grounds, where minor details, like different numbers per side, didn't matter.

They were covering two hundred and fifty to three hundred miles a day, well up to schedule. They drove an hour each, such having been decided for optimum attention span. The medical advisor insisted that everyone walked around for a minute at each stop, then seats were changed so that the comfortable bed on top of the stores in the back and the uncomfortable middle seat in the front were shared equitably. They took a full hour's break at lunchtime, although the ration of tinned cheese and water-biscuits was consumed in less than half that time; then the soccer ball was produced for mandatory fitness maintenance - five minutes two-a-side, and twenty minutes retrieving ball from trees and streams.

Yugoslavia was the first place that felt really foreign. North of Zagreb corn was being cut with sickles and scythes in small plots around the villages, a strange contrast to the combine harvesters working two or three abreast on the collective farms nearby. In a hedgeless countryside, cattle were chained together in small groups to graze under supervision. Road signs were markedly more difficult to pronounce.

That Saturday evening the sky was very dark and threatening as the tents were pitched between the road and a belt of forest. Supper was scarcely finished when the storm broke. And what a storm! Throughout the night the thunder and lightning hardly paused, nor did there seem an end to the deluge. They lay awake for hours, waiting for some disaster, but to their surprise the tents came through the trial with leakless credit. The downpour abated just before dawn and there was a heavy silence. Jim, who had remained awake after the others, was at last drifting off to sleep when there was a squelchy rustling outside and something brushed against the tent. Perhaps a wild boar from the woods? Didn't they attack people? Would a loud shout be more likely to frighten it off, or enrage it?

"Psst!" said the boar.

"Hello?" said Jim. A head appeared through the tent-flap.

"Good morning! I thought you were a boar," said Jim.

"Hello," said the head, "how is King Peter?"

The head belonged to a man who seemed quite elderly. The others awoke and offered him breakfast, but he wouldn't stay; he wanted to be away from people driving a British jeep before he was seen by neighbours. When the German army had occupied Yugoslavia twenty years before, he told them, he had been sent to fight in Finland. After the war he returned to find Marshal Tito ruling the country. "He took away ten acres of my little farm for redistribution, and I pay a heavy tax on the rest." But he was sure that some day King Peter, exiled in London, would return and right all wrongs. "Do you know him?" he asked excitedly. They said that unfortunately they didn't. He shook each of them by the hand and disappeared into the mist.

The rain which still fell intermittently discouraged porridge-cooking, so they made do with biscuits, packed up and got going. A few miles further on they were slowed by streams of people walking along the wet road, heading towards a large church. Communist countries did not have a reputation for encouraging churches, and the two theologians decided that the Expedition should start its first Sunday by joining the congregation.

The church was old. The walls were about five feet thick but this had not prevented the damp from penetrating many of the gospel scenes painted inside. But what first struck the four was the absence of seats; everyone stood, or kneeled on the stone floor. There were about a hundred children at the front, some five hundred women behind them, wearing black embroidered aprons and colourful headscarves, and men filled the rest of the space at the back, on the balcony and in the porch. There were no books and there was no musical accompaniment to the singing; one of the women would sing a phrase, the rest of the women would harmonise in the next one, and then the rich throbbing bass from the back would come in. The whole service was sung in this way, and, although they couldn't understand a word, the four travellers found it deeply moving. After the service they asked one of the men, who could speak as much German as Jim could, how a seemingly small community in a communist country could pack a church to overflowing. He shrugged. "It is *our* church," he told them. "True, we are forbidden to take collections or perform baptisms in the church, so we give the priest gifts of food and have our children baptised at home." In the bigger towns there was more pressure to discourage Christianity, but it thrived in the countryside.

There seemed to be an amazing mixture of religions, with Catholic predominating in the North and elsewhere larger proportions of Orthodox churches and Islamic mosques. Andrew reflected that the poor atheists must feel terribly outnumbered. Racial variety reflected the religious. School history lessons came fuzzily to mind, with their dark references to conflict between Moslem and Christian, bitter wars between Croats, Serbs and Slavs. Richard wondered aloud how Tito managed to keep the place together.

Southeast of Zagreb they joined the 'Autoput', which looked impressive on the map, but most of it was not even dual-carriageway. At one point they were surprised to meet a herd of cattle coming towards them - "How refreshingly different from our M1," muttered Jim, taking avoiding action. Other differences from the M1 were the number of hay carts and pedestrians. Traffic was light, however, so Charlie averaged a creditable forty miles per hour. The vast Yugoslavian plain, with its occasional slow muddy rivers heading for the Danube, rolled past in the drizzle until they saw signs to 'Beograd', which inspired David to recite:

"An Austrian army, awfully arrayed, boldly by battery besieged Belgrade."

"Cossack commanders cannonading come," Andrew joined in, "dealing destruction, devastating doom."

"A public school education is a wonderful thing!" sighed Richard.

"I wish we had been taught history better," said Andrew. "Here we are in the cauldron of the Balkans, surrounded by the raw material of continual conflict, and yet I haven't a clue why there was always a war going on!"

"I blame religion," came Jim's voice from the back.

The distant hills were shrouded in cloud as they drove through a dreary Belgrade. It kept raining, so they kept driving. By two o'clock in the morning they had completed 440 miles, which was to remain the record for a day. The rain had stopped so they stopped too, and slept beneath a tarpaulin in a lay-by just short of Nis.

The metal floor was hot to the touch as they whined up the muddy hill in bottom gear, edging past the occasional bullock cart. The AA route notes had warned them that roads deteriorated after Nis. There, they had dutifully written postcards in the sun, and had tried to converse with a small group of youths on bicycles - without finding a common language. Few people seemed friendly in the towns; it was different in the countryside, where walkers would wave or raise their hats to Charlie. Not that there were many walkers on this dirt road in a thunder storm. The rain hammered on the roof and dribbled in at the window corners; the road was a river and visibility was a matter of yards. Richard slipped the lever into four-wheel drive for a particularly steep muddy bit. They breasted the hill and suddenly found themselves on a broad tarmac surface. At the same time the deluge stopped, and there in the wet distance, towering above the landscape, were two white concrete buildings of unusual size and modern design, strangely incongruous in the rural setting. The two ugly sisters turned out to be customs posts, doing their best to impress each other across the frontier between Yugoslavia and Bulgaria. There were few travellers and plenty of staff, but it took over an hour to undergo the paperwork. The Bulgarian side was the worse, with officials who refused to speak anything but (presumably) Bulgarian. Under the red flags and huge portraits of Lenin and Kruschev, the Expedition felt well and truly behind the Iron Curtain.

Then away down the Dragoman Pass, where Attila and Hannibal and Alexander had no doubt trod, although they weren't sure if Hannibal came this way, or if Attila hadn't been further to the North, and Richard thought that Alexander went East, not West. But they were agreed that countless splendid figures must have gazed upon this view on their way to add a bit of carnage to the Balkans.

Presently, roadside statues of scythe-wielding peasants announced the approach of Sofia, and they braced themselves for another dose of red flags and oppressive portraits. But Sofia was a pleasant surprise - set among parks and trees were the first buildings of notable beauty they had seen since Austria. They stopped in the afternoon sunshine to look around. The clothes in the shops seemed expensive, and the citizens rather dour. With large numbers of armed soldiers around, it was hard to feel relaxed, and they could not help but remember that, only two years before, war with the Eastern Bloc had seemed a real possibility. At that time, the 1962 Cuba Crisis, nuclear war had seemed so likely that some students had given up working for exams, reckoning such trivialities unimportant. Brian had announced he would not bother with lectures because he wanted to finish his James Bond novel before the world ended - mind you, Brian didn't bother going to lectures anyway. A clique of the College's more zealously religious had drawn up a list of those likely to qualify for the Afterlife (presumably to save the Almighty time and trouble) - an unpopular exercise amongst those who found their names didn't feature!

"Why does everyone scowl at us?" asked David.

"Yes, it is a bit uncomfortable! But don't forget," said Jim, "that they have been taught to regard Westerners as the enemy."

Not wishing to attract further attention, the enemy returned to Charlie and pressed on. Unfortunately, they missed the signpost on the way out of Sofia and became wedged between two trams in the middle of what had been, before they stopped the traffic, a very busy intersection. Large numbers of uniforms appeared.

"Don't let them know we're Westerners," David whispered.

"Plovdiv road?" asked Andrew, smiling nicely.

With much shouting and arm waving the uniforms organised a communal reversing and turning exercise, and it appeared by the gestures that they were to follow a lorry full of soldiers. They weren't sure if this was good news. They waved cheerfully at the lorry, and all the soldiers quickly looked away.

"Maybe this is the Plovdiv road," murmured Andrew hopefully, as they bumped along the cobbled city streets. The others suggested alternative explanations, featuring phrases like "internment camp" and "never to be seen again". Gradually the buildings thinned out, until they were in the countryside once more. To their surprise, all the soldiers in the back of the lorry now waved and smiled, and their driver signed them to overtake. Soon they passed a signpost to Plovdiv, and the afternoon seemed warm and pleasant.

Camping was forbidden, the guide-book said, save at authorised sites. There was no other traffic about when Richard, who had the map, directed them onto a winding dirt road.

"Where's this?" asked the others.

"Looked interesting," shrugged Richard. After a mile or so they came to a wide clearing in the middle of nowhere.

"Camp site!" said Richard.

"Authorised?"

"I doubt it," grinned Richard.

The evening was cool, but it was too much trouble to put up tents. They sprawled in their sleeping bags around the petrol lamp, writing or dozing or thinking. It was all very restful until Jim, with his medical hat on, produced the spade and toilet roll, and delivered a lecture on the importance of regular bowel movements. Evidently their performance of late had been below quota. Awareness of the surreptitious interest of others, however, was a definite inhibition, and morning dawned on spade and paper in the middle of the clearing, apparently untouched.

Plovdiv came and went. Roads were not good. They winced for Charlie as they bumped along the ruts, trying to avoid the worst pot-holes. Twenty miles an hour was for the better bits, and they seemed to be moving little faster than the horses and carts that made up the bulk of traffic. David was in an Eeyore mood, brooding on their slow progress, worrying about schedules and boats. What if they couldn't get to Africa?

"Look on the bright side," Jim pointed out, "we've covered seventeen hundred miles in less than a week, seven countries in seven days. And I'm sure that there will be a boat when we get to Jordan."

"But what if it leaves the day before we get there?"

"If we break a spring trying to get there a day earlier we'll get there a week later!" growled Richard.

Ahead of them an old car was jacked up on the roadside, and someone was struggling with a flat tyre. They stopped, and found another Cambridge student, Jock from Clare, who hoped he was on the right road for Greece. Having got the Stanley and Livingstone bit over, they sorted out the Lancia ("It cost £39," Jock told them proudly), exchanged news from the homeland, shared some biscuits and tinned cheese, and parted towards the next set of potholes. They tut-tutted over Jock's lack of tools and spares, his inadequate maps and vagueness of game-plan.

"These young people have no idea!" sighed Andrew.

The nearby fields seemed to be worked exclusively by elderly women; or maybe they just seemed old. The tall avenues of poplar and plane trees which fringed the road were beginning to give a better impression of Bulgaria when a succession of loud red banners, exhorting hard work and vigilance and brotherhood and other Orwellian themes, spoiled the effect. The officialdom at the frontier with Turkey completed their dislike of Bulgaria. Queuing and form-filling again took over an hour. Scowling uniforms were everywhere. The Expedition was sure that the flocks of functionaries were only pretending not to understand anything in English. Andrew could sense the others' rising irritation, and was particularly anxious lest David would tell his "vulgar Bulgar" joke.

Their hearts lightened once the barrier swung down behind them and they trundled across to the Turkish side, free of the Iron Curtain. Even the equal delays going through Turkish formalities didn't dent their spirits. The Turkish roads, however, were no better than the ones they had left. As Charlie climbed slowly through the treeless uplands, signs saying "YAVAS!" were frequent, shortly followed by precipitous hills, narrow bridges, severe bends and the occasional overturned bus. They camped among fireflies. Andrew was asked why he wore his glasses at night, and explained that if he went to sleep without them he couldn't see the stars. They gave this some thought, but not too much.

"Wake up!" called Richard at 6 a.m., "Only a hundred miles to Istanbul!" Enthusiasm before breakfast can be very irritating, and there was hostile reference to the Ipswich Scouts, but they were on the road in good time. Most of the other traffic seemed to be military, and they remembered that this was the NATO frontier. When they met four tank squadrons in convoy, Jim was inspired to recall the halcyon days when his Conqueror churned through the Rhineland, inadvertently nudging lamp posts to ruin. He sighed and gazed across the rolling hedgeless ground - wonderful tank country! He would have his troop hull-down behind that ridge........ The others, deprived of National Service days, made unkind remarks about playing soldiers, whilst engaging in secret envy.

"Didn't the Germans hate you tearing through their crops and knocking down bits of their villages?" asked Andrew.

"When we were on exercises, creating this mayhem, there was always someone following behind with a cheque book," said Jim, "so

I suppose that softened the anger. But, yes, they must have hated us telling them it was for their own good. Just as the French can't have enjoyed being bombed by the British in Normandy."

"Isn't it sad to be British," mused David, "saving the world from Fascism and Communism, and being hated for it!"

They drove into Istanbul at lunchtime. The traffic density surprised them, as did the lack of any apparent highway code. The horn was king, and their klaxon held its own with the best of them as they wove over the cobbles between rickety wagons and large American cars. A few spectators dressed as traffic policemen watched the happy chaos. The Banka Centrale was their prime objective, for money and mail, but it was having a lunch break. To fill the time, they wandered down narrow back-alleys, letting their nostrils feast on the cocktail of woodsmoke and sewerage and spices. Ramshackle sheds, surrounded by a scattering of barefooted children, may look rather sweet in a rural setting, but when the hovels are stories high and packed together, and when they extend for miles through a smelly city, the quaintness fades. Certainly the squalor dismayed the four at first, but after a while distaste was replaced by fascination with the hive of activity behind the facade. It seemed that every building had a workshop on the ground floor, some with huge wooden looms weaving carpets, some engaged in copper-work, others making quilts or baskets or shoes. Similar trades seemed to be grouped together in a street.

The Expedition, now pestered by a pack of ragged urchins requesting money and cigarettes, retreated to the Mosque of Suleyman the Magnificent. Suddenly the heat and noise and smell and conspicuous poverty were wiped out, and the world was made of cool domes and marble pillars. It was an amazing juxtaposition of ugliness and beauty, utter poverty and incredible richness cheek to cheek. Everything was extreme, no happy medium, unlike England, where everything was in moderation. Or was it mediocrity?

They returned from the marble to the dust a few yards outside, and dutifully bought tourist post-cards. It took about an hour to find their way back to the bank and Charlie, and then they were on a ferry crossing the Bosphorous - leaving Europe for Asia.

"Isn't this exciting, plunging into the unknown wastes and

uncharted dangers, facing fearsome hardship!" mumbled David through an ice-cream. Andrew grunted, preoccupied with the letter from home which he had just collected.

"Listen to this," he said, "they have heard from the London shipping agent, who says the only thing to Mombasa this month is a passenger ship from Beirut. But the fare is £400 each, which we can't afford, and in any case it can't take vehicles." There was a heavy pause.

"So," said someone quietly, "we'll just have to find another one!"

Chapter Three - Into Asia Minor

"No salad East of the Bosphorous," Jim instructed, referring to his medical notes, "or soft-skinned fruit, and boil all water." They had camped in a sandy gully just off the main road. It was not an ideal place, but it had taken a good while to find their way out of Istanbul and then they had stopped to swim in the Sea of Marmara. Dusk caught them short of where they expected to be, not that they expected to be anywhere in particular, except that they had not expected to camp by a main road. Turkish drivers used their horns more than their brakes, and it promised to be a noisy night.

"No soft-skinned fruit, as requested!" announced Richard, serving out the spam fried in butter, smothered in spaghetti, embellished with a topping of beans. "But wouldn't fruit be healthier than everything out of packets and tins?"

"Yes, we can eat oranges and bananas," said Jim, consulting his brief, "which are thick-skinned. Oh yes, finally, we don't swim in fresh water from now on because of Belhazia."

"Belhazia?" asked David.

"Blood parasite," Richard told him. "Nasty weakening result. Spread by fresh-water snails. My aunt is matron of a hospital in Egypt, where just about everyone has it."

"And now for the good news," continued Jim, "tonight with our Complan we start the Chloroquin anti-malaria tablets."

"Isn't it funny," mused Andrew, inspecting his spam for parasites, "we worry about snakes and lions, when the real danger is from things you can't see."

They rowed out the camp-beds alongside Charlie - tents were too much bother - and tried to sleep. The vehicles on the near-by road continued to speed past, exercising their horns.

"At least they drown the uproar of the crickets which might have kept us awake," yawned Jim. No reply. The others were asleep. The night was warm. Then something moved in the bushes by the road. Should he wake the others? There was a shape, black against the intermittent lorry headlights. He eased himself slowly out of his sleeping bag and crept towards the road. There was a ditch in the way, so he stood up and jumped across, then crouched again to listen. Nothing moved in the bushes ahead. He waited, straining to hear any noise that wasn't traffic, to see any shape that wasn't a bush. Maybe he had mistaken shadow for substance. The guide-book should not have mentioned bandits in Turkey. He looked back at the sleeping shapes by the Land Rover - so vulnerable. We really should keep a watch, he thought. He walked back and lay down, but could not sleep. Two o'clock showed on his watch. Then three o'clock. Then there *was* something nearby - a sort of panting and a snuffling. He shot upright. The dog at the end of his camp bed started to bark, and went on barking, minute after minute. David woke up, and sat up. The dog, still barking, retreated.

"That was going on for five minutes before you woke up," said Jim reproachfully.

"Was it? Why didn't it wake the others?"

"That's what's worrying! What if we were robbed?"

"That's why we lock the valuables inside Charlie."

"OK, what if we were attacked?"

"Who would want to attack us?"

"Go back to sleep!"

David did.

They could think of little but getting to Jordan and finding a boat, but their schedule called for the next morning to be dedicated to maintenance, and nobody wanted anyone to think they were panicking, so Richard changed round Charlie's wheels (so that they would wear evenly) and the others washed shorts and shirts, which dried fast in the hot sun. Then they drove on to Adapazari, a clean and pleasantly laid-out town on the river Sakarya. Since petrol stations were still frequent, the fuel cans on the front bumpers were being used for water, and these they refilled from a tap in the town square. A young man gave them a box of pears, refusing payment. They warmed towards Turkey. Pears, they decided, were to be classed as thick-skinned.

Finding the Ankara road (signposted Angora, which nearly confused them) they pressed on towards the hills. Turkish highways were always interesting: the occasional cart approaching on the wrong side of the road, children playing in the middle, cattle wandering across, a freshly-overturned bus, all kept the mind active.

That evening they stopped on a side road in the hills among pine trees, cunningly concealed from bandits. They had decided to post a guard - not that they were really worried, but they had agreed with Jim that they should be prudent in this slightly less civilised world, particularly since most of them slept like hibernating hedgehogs.

Andrew took the first two hours. He plugged their 12-volt lamp into Charlie's dashboard socket and brought his diary up to date, and then padded quietly round the Land Rover listening to the silence between the pines. He started to eat a pear, but the crunching made too much noise; besides, it was getting difficult to persuade himself that pears were thick-skinned. It was getting surprisingly cold, so he returned to the relative warmth of the cab and pulled a rug over his shoulders. Had he really done only one hour? He strained his ears for the slightest sound which tells the expert how big the bear is. He wondered if those scruffy chaps who had come past earlier were forestry workers. Richard had laughed and said that they looked just like brigands. Well, Richard could think about that when *he* was doing his stint. It was very quiet, wasn't it? He wished there was just a little background noise. In England there was nearly always some sound to live with: distant traffic, a radio, a door closing or an aircraft; here the trees seemed to be weighed down under the sheer weight of the silence. Why didn't one of the others snore or cough?

Jim completed the fourth watch and had the porridge ready at six. They left the wooded hills and headed across a vast plateau, which looked more like desert that farmland, although in the slightly less arid areas rows of combine harvesters were gnawing through sparse crops of corn. After the first hour they got tired of pointing and saying 'Oh look! There's another lorry upside down' and relapsed into a dozy contemplation of the horizon. The mandatory lunch-break and two-a-side soccer broke the monotony. Since lunch was invariably water-biscuits and cheese, speculation on which tin would be opened for supper provided the afternoon's excitement. Not that anyone was permitted to mention food until 4 p.m., in case they reminded each other how hungry they were.

The road became progressively worse. Driving involved intense concentration to weave a course between the potholes, while avoiding oncoming traffic doing the same thing. In early evening they left the plateau and began the long descent through the Taurus Mountains towards the Mediterranean. Now low gears down rocky gorges with violent bends slowed their progress further. There was nowhere which invited camping so they switched to the auxiliary petrol tank and kept going - until 2 a.m.., when enough was enough. They bedded down at the roadside, too tired to be disturbed by the heavy traffic - which would at least deter bandits.

Turkey had seemed very European hitherto, but they woke to a perceptible change. Trucks, horns blaring, were still the mainstay of the traffic, but now there were donkeys as well, trotting under impossible loads, and occasional strings of camels with deeply melodious bells. Suddenly Europe seemed further away.

Tarsus was reached at nine that morning. They sat a while in the hot sunshine speculating why horses and carts were carrying silt from the riverbed. A number of unlikely hypotheses were considered, but it would have been too much effort to actually ask someone. Turning East along the coast, they passed a couple of gaunt Crusader castles on rocky crags, before reaching the Gulf of Iskenderun, in the top right-hand corner of the Mediterranean. After a light lunch of biscuits and cheese ("Surprise!" exclaimed David) they rewarded themselves for the previous day's 400 mile stint by being tourists for an hour on the beach. A man on a tractor stopped and gave them three water melons. Now, water melons may be thick-skinned, but they were top of the Expedition's list of forbidden fruits, since they were often grown in areas of unsavoury effluents.

"No, really, how kind, but we're not allowed them," protested David. The man beamed.

"It's the dysentery, you see," explained David. The man nodded and gave them two more.

"Thank you very much indeed," said Jim. The man beamed and shook his hand.

"We shall give them to some deserving cause," Richard told him as he waved and drove off. "How awfully nice of him. I wish I could speak Turkish."

They swam in the warm sea, forgetting for a short while about boats to Kenya, or anything else for that matter.

The Syrian border-post was two miles beyond the Turkish one. It was not clear who owned the bit between. They had been pleasantly surprised by the Turkish officials, who were friendly and helpful - the first time they had encountered such behaviour at a Customs post! When they found nowhere to post their letters, a policeman offered to do it for them. Syria had a different approach - the imaginary queue.

"Form a line and wait your turn."

"But there is no one else waiting."

"You will be attended to when we are ready."

"Where can we change our Turkish Lira for Syrian money?"

"Maybe across the road." Andrew and David formed an imaginary queue to await the pleasure of a bored official while the others went across the road. Across the road was the Syrian equivalent of Joe's Transport Cafe, where a collection of shady individuals sat at tables with strangely-coloured drinks and piles of worn notes.

"Yes please, English money good."

"We have Turkish money to change."

"Turkish money not good." Nor was the exchange rate.

"But the official rate is much higher than this!" Jim protested. Shrugs all round. For some reason all the money-changers offered exactly the same rate, about twenty per cent less than expected. Jim and Richard considered waiting until they reached a proper bank, but they would need to refuel before then. Petrol was listed at the equivalent of only three shillings a gallon in Syria, so they had bought as little as possible in Turkey, and were now running short. There were additional reasons for patronising the local money-changers, who were numerous, sported conspicuous daggers, and seemed a bit thin on sense-of-humour.

Meanwhile the other two had discovered that if you fidget and re-arrange the pens and piles of paper on the Customs counter, or, apologising profusely, accidentally knock over the rack of passport stamps, you eventually unsettle a uniformed coffee-drinker into attending to you. Border posts, and a large number of flies, had made the Expedition rather irritable as it drove through the dry scrubby hills towards Aleppo, looking for a suitably remote camp site.

They were joined at breakfast the next day by a flock of black goats, accompanied by a flute-player. The flute was loud and shrill, the tune highly repetitive. Neither was conducive to the gentle easing into full consciousness that breakfast should ideally be. David got out the tape-recorder and pointed the microphone at the lad who was now interspersing the fluting with a strangulated nasal style of singing. When the playback button was pressed the goatherd's jaw dropped and, eyes staring, he stood listening; then he rolled around on the ground shrieking with laughter and slapping his thigh. Unfortunately he recovered and resumed his performance.
"Maybe the goats like it," suggested Andrew charitably.

They joined a reasonable tarmac road which took them through villages of beehive-shaped huts that seemed to be made of mud and straw. The occasional hut would have a Mercedes or a Combine Harvester parked outside, a modernity which contrasted strangely with the women carrying pitchers of water on their heads. In one village oxen were pulling a wooden sledge round and round over piles of cut corn; this threshing completed, the resultant pile of grain and chaff was winnowed - groups of men forking it into the air, where the wind carried the chaff away. It could have been a scene from thousands of years ago. For some reason they had expected something more modern - why, the Middle East was the cradle of civilisation after all, and right next door to Europe, but this part seemed as backward as Africa! Not that they had any experience of Africa yet, but everyone knew it was backward, didn't they?

The land grew drier and stonier between Homs and Damascus. Patches of scrub grew here and there on the flat plain, but it felt like a desert in the heat of late afternoon. Their double-roof did not prevent the impression that they were travelling in an oven, and the draught from the open windows soothed as much as a hair-dryer would. You could, Andrew observed, understand how the Psalmist sighed for green pastures and still waters.

At about 7pm, or it may have been about six or eight - they were unsure which time zone applied - a side track invited investigation. They were developing a nose for prospective camp sites. This one was an iron-ore quarry, and two aged gentlemen, who turned out to be brothers, emerged from a very small square stone hut and assured them in broken French that they were welcome to stay and to share their house. The Expedition thanked them - Andrew was rather good at French and delighted to find someone on which to use it - but, since it was hard to imagine fitting another four bodies into the hut, declined gracefully, saying that they would be quite happy sleeping in the open, if it was safe. Quite safe, the brothers assured them, and yes, in reply to the inevitable question, there were many snakes but usually quite small. This news was met with little enthusiasm, and the cooking had a watchful air about it. The brothers stood and chattered affably, but hastily said that they had already eaten when David proffered a mug of reformulated soup.

Their hosts employed about a dozen men to dig away at the hillside with picks and shovels, and then wheel-barrow the ore to a smelter in the nearby village. One brother was eighty-five and had fought in two wars. He disappeared into the tiny hut, shortly to emerge proudly in what they took to be his original uniform - knee-boots, baggy trousers, faded tunic, tasselled hat and ancient firearm. The Expedition expressed suitable admiration, but thought it diplomatic not to enquire against whom he had fought. The other brother enquired whether the four young men would like some coffee. The four young men expressed courteous enthusiasm and the octogenarians went back to their house. The night was warm and still. Jim was writing a letter, as usual. The others listened for snakes and watched the stars. There was no sign of coffee before they fell asleep.

"Coffee! Coffee!" The shout awoke them at dawn. The brothers beamed at the tousled heads emerging from sleeping bags and issued little glasses of warm sickly-sweet liquid that tasted unlike either coffee or tea. The Expedition smiled bravely, hoped the glasses were clean, and told anyone listening how good the coffee was.

"Why is it that city-dwellers are less friendly than country folk?" asked David. They had parked somewhere near the centre of Damascus, and were being regarded with more scowls than smiles. Andrew suggested it was because towns were less pleasant places to live than the country areas, so those who lived there were basically unhappy and scowled a lot. Jim pointed out that it might be that they themselves felt insecure among large numbers of strangers, and happier dealing with smaller numbers with whom they could communicate, so they only *thought* townsfolk were hostile. David said that was what a psychologist might say, and Jim said that was fighting talk. The others said they wanted to see Damascus.

Their guidebook told them that Damascus had the longest record of continuous habitation of any town in the world, a possible site of the Garden of Eden, and close to Abel's tomb in the nearby hills (Abel being part of the well-known Cain and Abel act). But then guidebooks were prone to exaggerate. The Old City area certainly didn't remind them of a Garden of Eden, the stench in some of the narrow twisting alleys making Istanbul seem perfumed.

"You're very quiet, Richard!"

"I'm trying not to breathe."

The cry of "Hello please, speak English!" introduced the inevitable youth who materialises in such places, endowed with a multitude of uncles (and sisters if necessary) anxious to meet them. His large family all seemed to be selling things in the maze of dark courtyards. The expedition admired the gorgeous hand-embroidered cloth and patterned copperware, but their guide lost interest when it became apparent they were looking, not buying. They wandered a while through the chaos of stalls and shops in mysterious little squares, carefully hopping over gullies of uncertain liquids and threading their way through loud throngs of peddlers and hawkers and purveyors of sweet sticky things.

It was when they returned to Charlie that Tigger had his tragic accident. Somehow he (tiggers lean to the male side of neuter) fell from the back door of the Land Rover into a shallow drain. Tigger had been donated to the Expedition by David's small niece, who feared in case the intrepid explorers might get sad and lonely, and need something to cuddle. The last thing Tigger was fit for at this moment was cuddling. What had occupied the drain before Tigger's arrival could be imagined, and the bedraggled stinking thing was relegated to the roof-rack for the next few weeks.

Andrew was driving as they squeezed their way down cobbled lanes packed with lorries and cars and donkeys and buses, with swarms of people filling the space between. He gritted his teeth in concentration as he wove slowly between the competition. Jim, with the map, offered words of encouragement as lorries overtook on the inside, horns trumpeting. He and Andrew got quite excited at one point when they drove down "The Street called Straight", which apparently had some biblical significance. Straight it was, but also narrow, made narrower by ranks of stalls on each side. However, they eventually broke free of the tangled warren and reached the lovely wilderness that flanked the road to Amman. No more would they denigrate the plains that looked like badly ploughed sea-shores. The sheer absence of horns and crowds was heavenly.

Two hours took them to the frontier, where the required formalities took a mere half-hour. The passport stamp told them they were in the Hashemite Kingdom of Jordan. Richard asked what a Hashemite was, but no one volunteered an answer. It may have been their imagination, but Jordan seemed better quality somehow than Syria. The houses seemed better-built, what land there was under cultivation seemed better tilled, the driving less frenetic and the horns less used.

"I think it's a historical thing," said David suddenly, half an hour into Jordan.

"What is?" asked someone not dozing.

"Horns, use of. The Turks and Syrians have traditionally been much trampled on, thus developing one huge inferiority complex requiring compensation; and so they use their loud horns to make them sound important. The Jordanians are culturally more dignified, desert-dwellers, not needing to make a noise to be noticed."

"What historical research supports your theory?" asked a voice from the back.

"Just a suggestion," sighed David. Silence returned, save for the even tenor of the engine and the hum of tyres on the road, which seemed better-surfaced than Syrian roads. The country through which they were passing was dry and hilly, the weather hot and sticky, yet the overall impression was of cleanness. Maybe it was just that Damascus was fresh in their minds. And, of course, they were carrying more than the memory of Damascus with them, for when they stopped stray strands of Tigger aroma drifted down from the roof.

An avenue of classical columns appeared over on the right.

"Jerash," said Richard, "Roman garrison town, rediscovered by a German archaeologist in the 1930s. You are looking at the magnificent colonnade between the gateway and the temple of Jupiter."

"You classicists do know your stuff!" said Andrew admiringly.

"It says all that in the guide-book," said Richard modestly.

The miles sped by, but there was no way they could reach Amman before offices closed, so the search for a shipping agent would have to wait until tomorrow. As the sun dipped towards the hilltops they reached the outskirts of the capital, and stopped to get their bearings by an orchard of fruit trees, a patch of green in the surrounding yellowness. It seemed as good a place as any to camp, so the Official Interpreter was sent to the flat-roofed house at the top of the orchard. Andrew returned with the news that English was spoken, that the son went to Cairo University, and that an English University was welcome to camp among the plum trees.

"Do you realise," grunted Jim later through a mouthful of spaghetti, "we have never yet been refused permission to camp anywhere? Aren't people kind!" As if to emphasise the point, the owner of the plum trees arrived with a basket of fruit. Plums, they decided, would be classed as thick-skinned for the moment.

After supper they sat round the petrol lamp, listening to the ponderous predictability of Beethoven's Fifth on the tape-recorder. "I used to enjoy music much more," said Andrew, "before I knew the secondary theme was due to re-appear in the woodwinds or something; now I have to concentrate and listen for it instead of enjoying it." The evening was getting cold. It seemed odd to be cold in Jordan in Summer, but they were in the hills here, where there was often snow in Winter. David's hand had swollen from a bite of some sort, and Andrew administered Savlon ointment and a plaster from the medical chest. Jim, squinting in the poor light, reread a letter from Sal. Richard was checking Charlie's log book:

"Do you realise we did our three thousandth mile this afternoon?" he asked.

"That's an average of two-fifty a day," said Andrew, "and no hitches!"

"Yes, the trip's horribly tame," growled David, "boring, boring, boring."

"The floor around the gear box gets very hot," said Richard, ignoring him. "We must check the oil level tomorrow."

Tomorrow - a boat. Or not. And if not, what? Nobody voiced their thoughts. The Land Rover had to get to Nigeria. Richard had to get to Rhodesia. They were committed to a survey which had taken months to plan. So many people had helped them; they could not possibly give up and return home looking small and foolish. "Four months in Africa? No, just four weeks on the Mediterranean; awfully pleasant, really. Educational Project? Well, it would probably have said only what everyone already knew, wouldn't it? Well, yes, *we* were disappointed too! No, we didn't build it up into something grand and heroic! Well I'm sorry if you feel let down." Oh dear, no. They had to get to Africa. But if there was no boat? Then it would have to be overland to West Africa. But they hadn't the right maps or visas for the Sahara countries. Oh, go to sleep and let tomorrow come.

The gleaming glass and concrete building had "Abu Zeid and Nazzal" in big letters over the door. This was the first address on the list they had just got from a very helpful British Embassy. They explained this to a lady at the enquiry desk. She picked up a telephone. "There are some men from the British Embassy here, Sir...................Yes, Sir." Several floors up, she led them from the lift down a long corridor to a door at the far end, a door which left the modern office block behind. They found themselves in a dark, untidy office, rather full of leather armchairs. As their eyes grew accustomed to the dim light they made out a small figure behind a large desk, who introduced himself as the Senior Partner, eager to assist any friends from the British Embassy. The Expedition self-consciously brushed down scruffy shorts and explained that they were only simple students trying to get to Africa. Small glasses of sweet coffee appeared, and the simple students perched uncomfortably on the edge of deep chairs while Jim outlined their quest. Then there was a long silence while the little man burrowed among piles of paper on his desk. They felt that their fate hung in the balance.

"Well, I have a boat from Aqaba on 25th. July which arrives Mombasa a week later," he murmured to himself. This was too good to be true, surely! They leaned forward tensely.

"Can it take the Land Rover?" asked Jim in a voice admired by the others for its calmness.

"Yes."

"Why, that's marvellous!"

"But," said the little man, "no passengers." Four faces fell as one.

"Couldn't you manage it somehow?" asked David in a voice sounding less than calm. Paper rustled for a while on the desk.

"Cargo boat. Takes no passengers."

"But we wouldn't need food and could live in the Land Rover."

"It takes no passengers." A long, long pause. "But, I know the Director. Great friend of mine. I will send a telegram to him."

"When would you know the answer?"

"The answer will be yes, my friend." He gave a wheezing chuckle.

"How much will it cost?"

"Not more than two hundred pounds altogether." That was better than they had feared.

"We can wire to England for the money."

"Yes, always have enough money. Often a penny is worth a pound of dignity. Don't spend it, but have it; it gives dignity." And his little red eyes disappeared into the folds of his face as he doubled up in a great wheezing spasm of laughter.

"Have you another ship if this one is no good?" Richard was being practical, as ever.

"Yes. But this one will be good."

They arranged to return in two days to confirm the details, and skipped down the several flights of stairs instead of waiting for the lift. They could hardly believe their luck. It looked like they would be on their way to Mombasa within a fortnight. That wasn't too long to wait. In the meantime Andrew and Jim wanted to do Jerusalem, and Richard and David were keen to go to a UNESCO Conference in Lebanon; so they could probably manage both. Wasn't life great!

107 degrees Fahrenheit made walking hard work. The Amman Land Rover Agent was impressed by their letter of introduction from the Solihull Head Office and produced the regulation thick, black, bitter-sweet coffee in tiny china cups of eye-bath size. With the coffee

came iced water, which they left, and chocolate, which they didn't. Charlie got booked in for the next morning to have a thorough check-up and service - goodness knew when it would get another. The Agent took them to his house to be introduced to his father, and they conversed politely in pigeon-French. The old man remembered well when Amman was a small village nestling in a hollow among the hills, he said, not the city they saw before them now, laid out with modern buildings in broad streets. They scanned the flat-topped houses of sandy stone climbing the surrounding ridges, and agreed that it was much more pleasant than Damascus.

The Roman Theatre they came across on the way back was remarkably well preserved - and indeed was still quite usable. David did Portia's "quality of mercy" speech from the bottom of the open hemispherical bowl, and was plainly audible from the rim. He explained sheepishly that someone had to do the heroines in a boys-school play.

"Co-ed schools have the advantage of teaching you that girls are as unpleasant as boys," said Jim thoughtfully.

"Gosh!" exclaimed Andrew, "is that true?"

An old man selling nuts appeared, insisting that all British tourists had plenty of money. "We're not ordinary tourists!" they assured him, retreating from his bony grasp. Returning, hot and tired, to the comparative coolness of their fruit orchard in the hills, they found their hosts waiting "en famille" at Charlie's corner of the plum trees, eager to share mint tea and conversation. Andrew had told them of the son at Cairo University, but hadn't mentioned the other nine brothers and sisters. The entire family were great fans of Egypt's Abdul Nasser, and politely asked how it felt to be a defeated country. The Expedition felt compelled to defend the homeland, and equally politely suggested that Britain had let Nasser "win" the dispute over the Suez Canal only to placate the United Nations. Besides, they said, Egypt seemed powerful only when compared with other Arab countries. This brought politely heated rejoinders that the Western World was dependant on Arab oil, which could be a more powerful weapon than armaments. The discussion was interrupted by sirens, as a cavalcade of army jeeps swept past the orchard, escorting a blue limousine.

"King Hussein," explained their hosts. "His palace is a few

miles outside Amman - makes it easier to defend. There have been assassination attempts, thwarted by Hussein's Bedouin soldiers."

"Weren't they trained by the British?" asked the Expedition, a trifle smugly.

"Yes," came the smiling return, "we admit the British are useful at times! But you are not popular with everyone - there was disapproval of the King's marriage to an English girl."

The afternoon was turning to evening. Nearby, the Bedouin were rounding up goats and sheep on the stony pastureland where they settled long enough to raise a crop of corn in the Summer, before returning to their beloved desert.

"Our land is not fertile," the University son said sadly. "There is an old story that the Angel Gabriel had two sacks of rocks; one he spread over the world, and the other he spread on Jordan!"

Richard and David had taken Charlie to the garage, and were doing most of the service themselves, since they seemed to know more about Land Rovers than did the local mechanics. Jim and Andrew sat in the shipping office of Abu Zeid and Nazzal, faces grim, listening to the Senior Partner. He had received a reply from the Norwegian company whose cargo boat was due at Aqaba; and alas, the law forbade it to carry passengers.

"How do people get from here to East Africa?" asked an exasperated Jim.

"They fly," replied Abu Zeid (or Nazzal) "unless they have a Land Rover." He smiled at them. "You must not despair, my friends. Remember the tortoise and the hare! I think there may be another boat from Aqaba that goes to Egypt, taking passengers, and then I can get you a passage to Mombasa later in August. Or, if you can get to Aden, there is a boat that will take you direct to East Africa before the end of August. Let me find you the best route. Come back in a week."

"But we haven't that much time," protested Andrew. "Can we not get to Mombasa any sooner?"

"No," said the little Arab in the creased suit. They were ushered to the door. "Remember the tortoise and the hare," he shouted after them, and doubled up with laughter.

Chapter Four - The Holy Land

The Dead Sea was a thousand feet below sea level - a thousand feet below the level of most other seas, that is. The lowest place on earth. And the travellers' spirits were on the low side, too. When they got too morbid, Jim would do a rather good imitation of Abu Zeid's wheezing cackle and remind them of the tortoise and the hare. But it was the not knowing. They could accept delay with relative cheerfulness if there was a ship at the end of it, but protracted uncertainty was altogether different, a sort of suspended animation, like floating in the Dead Sea, which they were.

An hour from Amman, half way to Jerusalem, the heat was stifling. A swim had seemed inviting, but swimming in high-salt buoyancy was difficult. Your feet kept coming out of the water and then you would tip sideways and get a face-full of stinging brine. It was easier to float on your back. With practice you could get both big toes into your mouth at once, as Richard observed - and then a gollop of salt soup when you overbalanced, as David discovered.

"You could pickle herring in this!" Andrew rubbed his smarting eyes, which only made them worse. The tourists who boast of their swim in the Dead Sea don't usually mention having to wade back through muddy verges, nor the attempt to get dry afterwards. The salt paste, fast hardening in the baking heat, is little affected by towels.

Rather regretful of their tourist impulse, they returned to Charlie, who had found a friend. A Jordanian Army Land Rover in desert camouflage was parked alongside, and a group of soldiers was admiring the winch. In no time there was a mutual admiration of Land Rovers in progress. A Jordanian Sergeant brought out a bottle of whisky and offered to show them round Jerusalem, but both were politely declined. The Expedition was just not in a sociable mood - maybe because the world was one in which you couldn't get to Africa, and where salt got in your eyes.

The climb out of the rift valley serpentined through stony hills baking in the heat. Charlie's engine was "pinking" badly on the poor fuel, and they had to remain in bottom gear. Richard suggested a stop to retard the ignition. The others, wondering what he meant, agreed, and Richard proceeded to impress them by the necessary retardation. On they went, pinking less.

The theologians had thought it chronologically appropriate to do Bethlehem before Jerusalem.

"It's not as I imagined it," said Andrew. The Church of the Nativity was swarming with tourists.

"It's a very grand building," said Richard, "but something like a stable would have been better, don't you think?" They did. The University of Dublin Expedition to the Middle East, taking refreshment by the Bethlehem roadside, agreed with them.

"But it's better than Egypt," the Irishmen assured them. "Flies, red tape and having to sit up all night to stop your door handles disappearing. And you think this heat oppressive? Wait 'til you get to Egypt!" David said they would risk that, if a ship going to Kenya wanted to call there. Having remembered their plight, they got quite gloomy again, bade farewell to the Dublin lot and headed for somewhere quiet.

Andrew awoke. The Bethlehem hills were cold and grey in the predawn, with not a shepherd in sight. It had seemed an ideal place to camp last night, well away from everywhere, or so they had thought. Yet within minutes of getting the stove going they were surrounded by people; little groups emerging from nowhere, gathering round and watching silently. You turned to get a tin-opener, and fell over a new arrival; you tried to eat your soup facing a line of knee-caps at a range of thirty inches; ranks of eyes stared as you got into your sleeping-bag. You tried to smile in a friendly way and say "Good-night!" but still they stood and watched impassively, finally melting away reluctantly into the dusk. Very unsettling. And spoons disappeared. Not many, but you didn't have many.

"Why were you laughing in your sleep?" Richard asked.

"Was I?" Andrew frowned. "Oh, I think I was dreaming about the Emmanuel Sixth Boat last year, when we sank by The Plough!"

"I keep dreaming about boats, too," said Jim, "usually shipwrecks! What would a psychologist make of that?" David moved a morsel of biscuit and honey to the other side of his mouth.

"Well, I think Freud said shipwreck dreams represented anxiety about a love affair," (Jim's eyebrows rose) "but then he wasn't always right."

"Say so! Why not anxiety about getting a boat to Africa?" retorted Jim. "Seems more likely to me." He was going to further demolish psycholgists, but at this point they had to move the breakfast remains to allow a man on a donkey to pass, followed by a woman walking behind.

"In these lonely hills," muttered Andrew, "how did we manage to camp in the middle of a public thoroughfare?"

Hebron was next on the itinerary. The non-theologians among them complained a bit about paying five shillings to visit the tombs of Old Testament worthies, but, as they removed their shoes and joined the queue behind the lengthy retinue of an elderly Sheik, Jim pointed out that getting Abraham, Isaac, Rebecca, Jacob and Joseph all for five bob wasn't bad.

"I thought you said that most of them were not actual historical figures," David objected, "but more the stuff of legend, like King Arthur."

"Well, I did say that the history of the Aramaic tribes had been passed on verbally for hundreds of years before they were written down," admitted Jim, "and therefore one couldn't place too much reliance on the details."

"So, in these tombs, whose bodies are we admiring?" Richard pursued.

"And why are Old Testament figureheads in a mosque, not a synagogue or a church?" asked David. The theology department closed ranks and explained patiently the common roots of Judaism, Christianity and Islam.

"So why do they always seem to be in conflict?"

"How much time have you got?" sighed Jim.

On to Jerusalem at last. It didn't seem any different to other Jordanian towns, which surprised them because they had been expecting something special. Maybe the image created by Sunday School stories was overdone.

"Where do we camp?" asked Andrew, at the wheel.

"That hill looks a good spot," suggested Richard. Jim consulted the map.

"I think it must be the Mount of Olives. Turn down next left, by the Brook Kidron, and then next turning right, after the Garden of Gethsemane."

Charlie toiled up a dusty track and stopped beneath cool pine trees. There was a lovely aromatic resin smell, and a fabulous view down over the city. They wondered why there was nobody around. After lunch (Ryvita biscuits and Bovril, for a change) they dozed in the shade and listened to the distant sounds of Jerusalem below.

"It's funny," murmured David, hat over eyes and back to a wheel, "how we used to go to the beach near home in Summer and think it was hot......... The rocks seemed warm when you came out of the sea. We used to think we enjoyed seaweed and stones .... never even thought of going away for a holiday. No, thousands of grockles from England came to us for their holidays .... pouring out of their tourist coaches and crowding our beach, braying loud Northern accents.......... ."

"David?"

"Yes?"

"Shut up."

"Oh. All right."

The trouble with siestas is having to wake up afterwards. The theologians were reminded of Sheeol, that state of suspension of living from which consciousness was a temporary escape, according to the Pentateuch or something. They stirred themselves and walked slowly down the hot rocky road, past the Bougainvillas cascading over the Greek Orthodox walls of Gethsemane, and on up the next slope towards Jerusalem Central.

Andrew and Jim seemed strangely quiet, maybe because this had been the setting for the momentous events that would probably determine how they spent the rest of their lives. Richard and David were merely fascinated with the place. All of them were ready to approach Jerusalem with reverence, if not awe. But Jerusalem was not going to co-operate by seeming significant. It had no intention of being impressive, and appeared quite callous to anyone's need of inspiration. True, there was no shortage of Official Guides to direct them to Official Sites of Significance, but once a Holy Place was reached there was no opportunity for reflection or veneration. Instead, hordes of crucifix-sellers, professional beggars and spivs vied noisily for attention.

"This way for the Ascension Chapel! Don't be fooled by the Eastern Orthodox Ascension Church next door, because their's isn't the *real* site.Want to see the last footstep of Christ, Sirs? Four of you? I make special price. Very cheap. There now! You are looking at the actual Last Footprint, quite clearly imprinted in the ground. Yes, young man, it has indeed survived the years remarkably well. No, we don't refer to it as a take-off point. What do you mean, where's the next-to-last footprint? Don't be disrespectful!"

Throngs of the faithful, the pious, and the bored were herded around the shrines recommended by their sects, gasping at the tales of miracles ("yes, on this very street!"), patronising the tourist-memento traps, and worshipping the gimmicks lined up for them. Some parties were following the Stations of the Cross ("Yes, this alleyway is the exact spot Madam"), kneeling, weeping, chanting, praising.

"Can we go back now? I feel a bit sick," growled David eventually. "And I'm sorry I was rude to that priest who wanted to take us round - provided we made a donation to his Order."

"Don't worry," said Andrew, "Christ threw out the money-changers, remember?"

"Try not to let the tourist trappings put you off completely," urged Jim, "there's far more to get out of Jerusalem. But I think it needs time."

They sat under the pine trees and watched an orange sun set over the Old City. Here no one had arrived to watch them eat. Distant sounds floated up from below, but the hilltop was deserted and strangely quiet. They wondered why. Richard went for a wander, but soon returned to say he couldn't get far before barbed wire blocked the way. They all went to see, and fifty yards away they came across trenches and camouflaged pill-boxes, all silent and deserted. They hadn't realised that the Mount of Olives was on the border between Jordan and Israel, but it seemed peaceful enough.

Saturday, July 18th., dawned chilly; but it was warm by the time they passed the Dead Sea on the way back to Amman. They were going to see Abu Zeid, just in case he had heard anything. He hadn't. "Perhaps another few days," he said. "Yes," they agreed quickly, "the tortoise and the hare, we know." It was very hot as they passed the Dead Sea on the way back to Jerusalem, but no one suggested stopping for a swim - they were still coated with salt from the last time.

"Lowest place on Earth," Richard read from the guide-book, "part of the big fault that also formed the Rift Valley in Kenya."

"Well, fancy that!" they said, wondering if they would ever get to see Kenya.

The theologians' appetite for the Holy Places remained insatiable, so that afternoon it was back to the Via Dolorosa, David and Richard following dutifully but with less enthusiasm. The little cobbled alleyways and flights of narrow steps, the crowds around the stalls, the barefoot children playing with their hoops and kites, the usual noise and smells were all fine; it was the inside of buildings that depressed them. The Holy Sepulchre should have been inspirational, but was spoilt by being split up into little chapels and corners guarded jealously by the various denominations, each one touting for business as competitively as the postcard sellers outside. The Franciscan Chapel commemorating the Scourging of Christ was beautiful in its way, but again the walls and icons seemed to detract from, not enhance, the significance of the place. Everything had been made so utterly different from nineteen hundred years before. They wished they could have seen what it had looked like before being encased in brick.

They felt they should pay homage in some way to the place Jerusalem should have been, so the next morning they went to Sunday Communion at St. George's Cathedral. Then Richard and David and Charlie left for Beirut to find the UNESCO Teachers' Workshop, leaving Andrew and Jim to soak up the meaning behind the Holy City's sideshows. They also left them the tents, the petrol stove and four days' food supply on the Mount of Olives, which they now felt to be their exclusive territory. Each pair felt they had the better bargain.

It was getting dark as David and Richard stopped at the fourth customs post of the day. They were two hundred miles further North, and had successfully negotiated the long arid roads either side of Damascus. They changed drivers once more, Richard taking the wheel to head into the dim remains of the Lebanon sunset. David was almost asleep when suddenly Richard spoke - quietly, but with an intensity that brought David awake in an instant.

"I think there's something in here with us."

"What do you mean?"

"I've just felt something go over my foot."

"I can't see anything in this light. Where's the torch?"

"Don't move. It's on my leg. I think it's a snake."

Neither of them spoke for what seemed a very, very long time.

"O.K.," said David very quietly, so as not to alarm the snake, "slow down gradually, and stop."

"And then?" came through Richard's clenched teeth.

"We get out fast."

"That's fine for you to say. You don't have it on your leg," he whispered.

"Right. We wait until it moves off. Then you give the word and we jump." Charlie was slowing now. The road was deserted. Ahead was a wide level corner.

"I can't feel it now," said Richard with icy calm. "I'm going to stop here." Charlie eased to a halt. David gripped his door handle with damp palms. He could feel his pulse pounding in his ears.

"NOW!" yelled Richard, and they leapt out of the doors and rolled across the tarmac.

"I wonder how the others are getting on," Andrew said through a mouthful of tinned sausages. They were back on the M. of O. after an afternoon in Nehemiah's Tunnel. This was cut through five hundred yards of solid rock, taking water into the city from the Pool of Siloam. It must have enabled the ancients to withstand a lengthy seige. Andrew had wondered aloud whether they were risking Belhazia as they waded along, but Jim had retorted that a far greater risk to health came from eating water melons. Andrew had again explained that it would have been very rude to refuse the kind gift. He hadn't intended to eat it, but the man had waited and watched, and

Andrew knew that Arabs could take offence if one didn't follow protocol. Jim had said that, since water melons tended to be grown on dung heaps, their protocol was not to eat water melons. After supper Andrew made frequent trips into the darkness with a spade.

Dawn was breaking in the Lebanese hills. Richard finished a Ryvita biscuit and rolled up his sleeping-bag. David was admiring his embryonic beard in Charlie's wing mirror. He was a bit annoyed that Richard's was much thicker, but then it had been started a month earlier. They put their stuff in the Land Rover and removed a length of rubber tubing from the pigeon hole by the steering wheel, from where it had half fallen the previous evening and brushed against the driver's leg in the darkness.

"I don't know why we brought it anyhow!" sighed David, starting the engine.

"Wasn't it in case we had to syphon petrol?" said Richard, applying TCP to his scratched knees and elbow. "And not a word to the others, O.K.?"

They checked the map. They were on the plateau between the Syrian border and the coastal mountain range. Two hours should take them to Beirut.

"Remind me why we are going to this UNESCO thing?" said Richard.

"Teachers from all round the Eastern Med and North Africa will be there to compare notes on using self-teaching programmes. We'll be able to find out what problems they've found in practice. The theory looks good, and the small-scale trials with maths seem successful, but it hasn't been much used in real situations. Anyhow, we may be able to get some useful addresses of African contacts from the people there."

"And I thought it was just an excuse to pick up the cigarettes!"

The road climbed over the coastal hills and then dropped three thousand feet to the coast. Approaching Beirut, they saw a notice saying UNWRA . They reckoned the UN part meant United Nations, and that they would know where UNESCO hung out, so drove into the compound. UNWRA was very helpful; they looked after refugees, but could lend them a guide to take them to the Teachers' Conference.

Their guide was a "displaced Palestinian". His grasp of English was imperfect, but he left them in no doubt of his feelings towards Israel. He told them that his town had sheltered some persecuted Europeans, who brought their friends; and then their friends brought *their* friends; and they then said it was *their* town and there was no room for Palestinians. He asked David how he would like to be thrown out of his home, where his children had been raised, to depend on charity.

"My son write poem. You take a copy for English newspapers - here!" It was a long poem, and pretty emotional, with verses like:

"No beats of a heart they wanted to hear
Nor a breath of a little child,
And the word of justice they always fear
For they are in evil's side.

Come on my brothers in East and West
Come on and hold up your lances.
It's a shame to sit down or to rest
Before the time of vengeance.

Say to life good-bye
My people everywhere.
Don't care to live or die
Say to life good-bye. "

"It's ...er....powerful stuff," said David when he had read it. "But can't you negotiate some compromise and share the land?"

"How possible to talk when say your home is now our home because God gave it us? But we will return some time. King Hussein and Abdel Nasser will get it back for us. 'Til then refugees, beggars." Tears ran down his face.

He was a large man, and sat between them with some difficulty in the Land Rover, directing a memorable drive through Beirut. There appeared to be no halt signs at intersections, nor any commonly agreed highway code. The loudest horn seemed to take precedent, and fortunately Charlie's was louder than most.

"This makes Turkey seem civilised!" grimaced Richard, as traffic overtook them on both sides. They were approaching a huge roundabout into which all roads seem to feed.

"Which way?" asked David, tensely gripping the wheel. Their guide leaned forwards earnestly, frowning slightly. He looked left, pointed right, and shouted "Hold to the directly!". Having held to the directly for some time, they turned round and approached Beirut from a different direction. Their guide grinned amiably and said he had never actually been to the UNESCO building, but knew exactly where it was. As each terrifying crossroad loomed ahead Richard would recite encouraging phrases like "Who dares, wins" and "He who hesitates is lost", and David would thank him through gritted teeth.

When they eventually found the place, the first person they saw was a colleague of David's from Sheffield, who was leading one of the Workshop courses. They greeted each other like unexpected brothers.

"James! How wonderful to see you! How is Harry?"

"Fine. Just fine! He's had his car washed!"

"And Hilary?"

"Doing great! Her rats love the attic, and John put her dog in the letter box."

"Oh good! "

"And Neville's engaged!"

"When...." broke in Richard, "when did you last meet?"

"Oooh..." David thought back. "Must be three weeks at least."

"Before I forget," said James, "I've got the Programmed Instruction address list for you, as requested!"

"That's great, thanks! I don't suppose we could beg another favour?"

"What?" asked James guardedly.

"Can we use your shower?"

"Of course! I had thought of suggesting it, but didn't like to offend you!"

"Good heavens!" exclaimed Richard, "Is it as noticeable as that?"

After ablutions had been completed at the Biarritz Hotel (superior rating at £4 a day, although the hot water was cold) they spent the afternoon at a Seminar on Computer-assisted Teaching Machines. Richard was unimpressed, and asked why people went to

Educational Conferences. "Just to make sure" said James "that nobody else has made much progress, either!"

They presented their letter from the tobacco company and collected two thousand cigarettes from the prescribed warehouse, after which a quiet stretch of beach was found for the night. Well, it was quiet to start with, but after a short while Beirut decided to honour the President or mark the Feast of the Prophet, or something, and there were fireworks and bonfires until the early hours of the morning. Which made them more taciturn than usual as they left Beirut at dawn and climbed in second gear back over the hills towards Damascus. They stopped at a Syrian village to fill the water cans, taking their turn at the pump with a queue of women with pitchers on their heads. It made them feel closer to Biblical times than they had ever felt in Jerusalem. There was another brief stop, in Damascus, to buy some oranges and fill up with petrol at half a crown a gallon, much cheaper than in Jordan. Two sets of mountains and two borders (and therefore four border posts) mocked any idea of getting to Amman, let alone Jerusalem, that day. The Lebanese bureaucracy took the prize for sheer volume of forms to complete. The technique of smiling inanely and shaking hands with anyone trying to write, which had driven exasperated officials elsewhere to expedite their departure, was a dismal failure. Plan B involved rearranging the office filing system; but this had to be aborted when revolvers were loosened in holsters. "No sense of humour, this lot," muttered Richard. The Syrian border guards were more affable, and presented the travellers with two cucumbers, which were politely accepted, to be presented to someone else when opportunity arose.

The road South from Damascus was becoming familiar. Its light traffic and lack of hills and corners made driving effortless, and hourly rotation of drivers was necessary to keep them awake in the huge unending brown flatness.They were still forty miles from Amman as dusk approached. Hot and tired, they assembled the camp beds by the roadside and made a frugal supper (water biscuits and marmalade). In the distance sporadic fires marked Bedouin camps, and the moon rose full over the stony land.

Jim and Andrew had spent part of the day at one of the traditional sites of the Cruxifiction, a rock formation not far from the city walls which looked from a distance like a huge skull (Golgotha meant "skull-like"). It was of course rather crowded with competing sects, retailing holy water and relics. More movingly beautiful, but probably less historically correct, was the Garden Tomb, endowed with a cave, green trees, and a merciful absence of souvenir-sellers.

Andrew had been well dosed with remedies ancient and modern, but these couldn't prevent the need for an early return to the vicinity of the spade. Andrew could keep nothing down or in for long, and Jim was getting worried, for it had gone on for more than two days. Dehydration could not be taken lightly in this climate, so boiled water with a bit of sugar and salt was prescribed. Maybe kaolin and entrovioform would work soon. Jim had resisted saying "I told you so" for which Andrew was grateful, but the others would be back tomorrow, and they could be abrasively tactless at times.

"Have you seen a single Public Convenience anywhere in Amman?" asked David in desperation. Richard, in equal discomfort, said not. They had liberally partaken of orange drinks as well as coffee at Abu Zeid's, and were feeling the effects as they walked back to Charlie through central Amman.

"I suppose people must use the side alleys. I wonder if there are bye-laws against it? How about this one?" said Richard.

They emerged feeling guilty but much relieved. Suddenly half a dozen jeeps raced down the street, sirens blaring, and soldiers with sub-machine guns leapt out and fanned across the road in threatening poses.

"Maybe it's a *serious* offence," David whispered. But the military didn't single them out for attention - they were clearing *everyone* from the street. A woman got out of one of the jeeps and went into a shop.

"What's happening?" Richard asked a bystander.

"Princess Muna," came the reply. "Shopping. Security."

They drove fast the rest of the way to Jerusalem, for they were in a hurry to share the news Abu Zeid had given them, and lunchtime saw Charlie grinding slowly up the hill to the Mount of Olives. Andrew looked a bit pale, the travellers thought.

"Well?" asked Jim.

"Well what?" grinned Richard.

"Come on, you are looking immensely pleased with yourselves. Let's hear it!"

"We've got a ship!"

Any Pharisee, Scribe or Zealot who chanced to be passing would not have understood why four adults were leaping around, laughing and shouting. Perhaps some phrase involving new wine might have occurred to them; or perhaps they would have thought that news of a miracle had arrived from the Jordan, in which case they would not have been far wrong.

"Belgian cargo boat!" cried David.

"Called the Mokoto!" cried Richard.

"We're deck cargo from Egypt to Mombasa - "

" - leaving Port Said on August 10th.!"

"Brilliant Abu Zeid! Long may his tribe increase!"

A huge weight had gone from their shoulders. True, they would not get to Kenya until August 20th., which would make the rest of their schedule hectic, but at least they would not have to skulk home with tails between legs.

But first they had to get to Egypt. The alternatives were a boat from Aqaba, leaving in two days time, or one from Beirut a week later. The choice was whether to spend the next week in Jordan or in Egypt. Jordan won, for there was so much more they wanted to see.

Since this would be the last night in Jerusalem, Richard decided he would do a special supper, including bread. The others started packing up for an early start the next day, but little got done, because suddenly their exclusive Mount of Olives territory became popular. A family driving to New Zealand (via India) arrived first. Their small Land Rover looked very fragile beside Charlie. Then a couple of Americans in a temperamental Volkswagon arrived for the view, stayed for coffee, and gave them a Monopoly set. Richard's bread was now ready for formal tasting. It looked a little on the solid side, but the assembled multitude all took their share. There was a time of concentrated chewing.

"Gee, it's revolting!" exclaimed the Americans.

"Isn't it?" beamed Richard, finishing off everyone else's.

It was dark before the Expedition had the place to themselves again. They sat round the petrol lamp and took stock of their finances. Being deck cargo on the Mokoto would cost only £130, so they had £150 in hand for the rest of the trip. That should be plenty, since their only regular expense was petrol.

Andrew sighed and left the tent for another pilgrimage with the spade. Shortly afterwards there came the sound of raised voices, and Andrew re-appeared, surrounded by grim-faced and heavily-armed soldiers. Language barrier notwithstanding, they got the impression tourists were unwelcome. Jim, putting on his fatherly voice, said that they would be leaving very soon, and Richard gave them the two Lebanese cucumbers (he was going to give them some of his bread, but was stopped just in time). The soldiers still seemed unhappy, but eventually left, scowling and repeating "Border forbidden".

"That was very embarrassing!" said Andrew. "I had dug my hole, and was just settling, when a torch shone in my face and I was looking down the barrel of a gun. Quite upsetting. Not at all dignified."

"Never mind, try the other direction now that they've gone," suggested Jim.

"I don't feel like it any more," frowned Andrew.

Chapter Five - Jordan and Lebanon

Charlie edged through the cobbled alleys, avoiding donkeys, stalls of sweet sticky things and hordes of small children, past the golden Dome of the Rock, and out into the countryside. The morning had been filled with letter writing, now that African schools could be advised of dates, and families at home told of the travel plans. Someone had said there was a postal strike in England, but maybe it would be over by the time their letters arrived. Jim had written a very long letter to Sal, assuring her that everything was going splendidly; David a fairly long one to a girl from Homerton, painting a picture of Stoic endurance in the face of adversity.

They headed away from Jerusalem, first to Ramallah, then onto the Nablus road. Reapers with sickles in hand worked in the roadside fields; camels with huge loads of straw bales provided a challenge to overtaking; a small boy herding goats was using a sling to direct stones at any strays - very biblical somehow. All the women seemed old and sour; but maybe that was because of the hard work and child-bearing expected of them. Jim and Andrew kept the others informed of pertinent historical details as they went. They passed Bethel (developed by Jeroboam on the traditional site of Jacob's ladder-to-heaven dream) and paused at the ruins of Shiloh (scene of the Samuel and Eli story). Richard said he wanted to see where the Philistines were slain with the jawbone of an ass - mass murder had always made scripture lessons more interesting. By now they were getting close to Nablus.

"Shechem is near here," said Jim, "the ancient city where the twelve tribes came together under Joshua about 1200 BC What is fascinating was the gradual ascendancy of Yahweh religion over Baal worship."

"Absolutely stunning!" grunted David heavily from the back.

"It really is," Andrew admonished him. "You see, the twelve tribes had a common Aramaean ancestry, but had probably been split up for hundreds of years, with some going to Egypt and some being assimilated into Caanan; so the odds were heavily against Israel becoming a nation at all, let alone developing a new religion!"

"There it is, Shechem, straight ahead," said Jim, checking the map. They stopped at the base of a high hill. There seemed to be a lot of activity going on.

"Hi there," called a piercing American voice, "I'm Mary-Lou; who are you?"

Mary-Lou turned out to be an archaeologist working on the site for the Summer. She seemed to assume that anyone from Cambridge would be eager to tour the excavations. Before Richard could say they hadn't had lunch yet, Mary-Lou was bounding up the hill, while they tried to catch up.

"This hill was a great place to build a city," panted David, to be affable.

"This hill is the city," retorted Mary-Lou, "or, rather, a succession of cities. See those mountains all around? Well, this was a pass the trading caravans used between the coast and the East. A city that controlled the pass controlled trade, so it was rich. The trouble was that invading armies travelled the same route, so a city didn't last too long! They built each new city on the remains of the last one, so the hill grew. To reach the past you just go vertically down! The bottom layer is about 3000 BC"

"What are you looking for?" asked Andrew.

"We think we've found it - the Temple of Joshua."

"El Berith," murmured Jim.

"Say, you're good! Yep, the God of the Covenant place! Those huge stones down there," she pointed into a pit about fifty feet deep, "were probably the Eastern Gate." While they watched, the packed mud - laid to absorb the shock of ancient battering rams - was being cleared from around the stones. The workers sifted each shovel-full, and separated out relics of the time, such as sling stones. The size of these was a surprise to anyone who had sung in Sunday School of the "pebbles" little David had taken from the brook. These sling-stones were the size of apples - Goliath didn't have a chance!

"We've found another temple on the same site about five hundred years older; probably destroyed by the Hyksos."

"I've never heard of them," admitted Richard "Who were they?"

"No one's quite sure," said Mary-Lou, "Probably of Asiatic

origin. But, boy, they were dynamite! Conquered the whole area, including Egypt. Now I've just got to show you - " and she was off like a mountain goat, bounding over the rubble and disappearing down trenches. Her four charges drooped along behind in the blazing sun, streaming sweat and wishing they had something better than sandals to withstand the camel-thorn. They inspected a child-burial - sacrificed at the consecration of a new house; they admired the black layer, unearthed only that morning, which Mary-Lou said was the burning of Shechem by Abimelech; they inspected olive-presses and seals and grinding-stones. So infectious was their guide's enthusiasm that after two hours heat and hunger were almost forgotten.

A warm wind gave but slight relief from the lingering heat. The moon bathed the valley in a silvery light, and gave the sky a dim purple tinge, against which rocky ridges were silhouetted. You never noticed the sky much when you lived in houses, but here in the open you saw it with fresh eyes, and it repaid the attention. The day had been well used. After Shechem they had visited a school in Nablus which had been using the Programmed Instruction method; the teacher in charge was still at the Beirut Workshop, but they got an idea of the practical problems of teaching there - having three rooms available to teach four hundred and seventy children would have been difficult enough, without the Moslem requirement to teach boys and girls separately! Then they had gone to Jacob's Well, a hundred and fifty feet of it, near the holy mountain of Gerizim (where Christ had asked the woman of Samaria for a drink). Finally, still baking in their oven-on-wheels, they drove down through the brown wrinkled hills to the Jordan valley for the night.

Next morning the schedule called for a final visit to Abu Zeid, and on the way they stopped at the ruins of Jericho. Time had built up the ground level, and you now peered down at the old walls where the desert dust had been dug away. They wondered how much ancient blood had soaked into the sand below.

Before reaching Amman they stopped to visit a teacher at a refugee settlement run by UNWRA. The school there, with eight thousand children, impressed them immensely - not for its facilities, which were rudimentary, but for the commitment of the Palestinian teachers. One of them explained "We have lost our country, our homes, wealth, way of life; all we have left are our children, and we must build their future on education. This is not just a job to us."

Abu Zeid - they never did find out his real name - presented them with their shipping documents. "Here is a letter of introduction. Find out about the Mokoto as soon as you get to Egypt, and leave five or six days spare - you can never tell with these Egyptians. Don't loiter, my friends, don't loiter! Remember the tortoise and the hare!" And he sent them on their way with much shoulder-slapping and cackles of wheezing laughter. They reckoned they had three days before they would have to leave for Beirut. "Just enough time for Petra," said Richard..

The Desert Highway towards Aqaba had quality - the best tarmac they'd seen for weeks. It also went through real desert, the only green being rare patches of thorn scrub; so they were not expecting much sign of life. Three hours South of Amman, they took great clouds of dust in the distance to be a wind storm; but as they drew closer they saw in the dust more animals than they had ever seen before in one place at one time. The focus of these vast numbers of camels and sheep and goats was a large pond of water, surrounded by low concrete walls, making it look a bit like a swimming pool. The herds and flocks were queuing for hours - or maybe days - for their turn to drink, after which they would drag their particular cloud of dust away into the desert whence they had come. Countless thousands of beasts milled around tented encampments in all directions as far as the haze allowed them to see. The expedition rummaged for cameras to record such an epic scene, but before much film could be used the uniforms arrived (whether police or troops it was hard to say) and shouted something about "forbidden". Protests were to no avail. One uniform which spoke English explained that Jordan was a progressive country, and didn't want pictures taken to give the impression that Jordanians were backward tribesmen.

Supper was taken in the middle of nowhere. They watched the sun edge behind an orange-glazed Western horizon, and a huge moon creep over the Eastern hills. The day-long wind had fallen to a cool breeze, and the desert was silent except for the hiss of the petrol lamp.

No one wanted to break the magic by speaking. They were all thinking they could happily stay here for a very, very long time; but they all knew the others were thinking the same thing, so there was no point in saying so. The dusk deepened. Eventually Jim broke the silence.

"It's funny, I never realised that the Expedition would be so ... so easy, so peaceful. I expected a bit more hardship really. ......I suppose in a way I'm disappointed that we haven't had our endurance tested...... OK, I know it's early days and it'll probably get more rugged at some stage!"

"Your turn to wash the dishes," said Richard.

Petra was hard to find. Richard, with the map, said it had to be somewhere nearby. They came across a rather severe gentleman with a museum musket, who directed them to a narrow gorge, cut through the rock by some long-extinct river. Andrew observed it was just the place for an ambush. They all laughed, and walked warily. Half an hour into the chasm, when they were wondering how much further it went, they came across a huge temple-like thing, with pillars hewn out of the pink rock. The facade could have been modelled on the Bank of England, but being miles down a chasm in the middle of the desert made it very much more impressive. For a minute no one spoke. It was really creepy! The place was deserted and silent in the mid-morning heat. Someone said "Wow!" under their breath - you didn't dare say it loudly in case something heard you. Hesitantly they went up the steps; nothing moved inside, so they edged in, and were both relieved and disappointed to find it extended only a few yards into the rock-face.

A little further along, the gorge emerged into a clearing in the surrounding hills, where there were many more temples and cave-houses. One or two dwellings were inhabited, but the general impression was of a lonely waste. Richard, who had been reading the guide-book again, told them that the Nabateans were former owners of this hidden fortress, and used to charge "protection" fees to travellers, of whom there were many since Petra was on the land-route between the Arabian Gulf and the Mediterranean. "And long before them, when the Exodus from Egypt took place, the Edomites lived here," added Jim.

They spent several hours wandering among the ruins, the skeleton of past empires, much weathered by the winds of centuries. Sky-blue lizards ran among the stones up on the heights, from where you could look down the rocky passages to the bowl below, baking in the noonday sun.

It was with reluctance that they trekked back up the lonely gorge. They wondered why the place wasn't teeming with tourists, but were heartily glad it wasn't.

The town of Ma'an, on the way back North, had a mosque and minarets that caused Andrew to compare it with a disguised rocket base. They had stopped here for the night because it was halfway to Amman, and were about to start on the macaroni and fried luncheon meat when the Dublin University Expedition showed up. Jim enquired how, since the desert was largish and Charlie was concealed from the road, Irishmen could detect when supper was ready? The Irish lot modestly yielded credit to their Arab guides, seconded from the Jordanian police, who evidently knew everything happening within fifty miles. Jim invited them to stay for a bite of supper, seconded by Andrew who hoped their sponsors included Guinness. One of the Arabs showed them how the Bedouin made bread, which Richard said was even better than his, and a pleasant evening passed.

After their guests had left, they wondered how the Dubliners had managed to get police guides. David asked whether anyone would really want a pack of Irishmen loose in their country without supervision. They then realised they had never asked them the purpose of their expedition. Presumably they would have had some objective?

Next day, Amman again, with its heaps of square boxes on the hillsides. They visited the new university, two years old and with two hundred and fifty students. Their contact in the Education Department was violently anti-Israel.

"How would you like guests in your house to decide it was now their house?" he asked. "Evicted Palestinians make up a third of the population of Jordan, and they are angry people. Those who have lost everything have nothing else you can take from them, so they are dangerous. Soon they will take back their own."

"But the Jews must also be allowed to live somewhere?" demurred Andrew. "They've been persecuted everywhere for so many centuries!"

"Why is it that those who have been bullied become bullies themselves?" came the retort.

They went for the last time to check for mail at the Ottoman Bank. The clerk asked them if they were Germans, and seemed disappointed when they said not. There was a letter from Brian which Andrew's folk had forwarded; Brian was now a high-powered executive-in-waiting. He kindly sent good wishes for their "mission to the dark continent", and said that he was presently suffering from piles, an experience which he described as "akin to giving birth to hedgehogs".

Women were gleaning in the stubble fields along the Damascus road as they left Amman. It was as if nothing had changed for thousands of years. The usual bureaucratic idiocy of the border-posts was endured on the way North. Passive acquiescence made for faster treatment, hurtful though it was to their pride. They were again asked if they were German - for some reason this seemed expected of bearded travellers in Jeeps. Then on across the arid, windswept plain. A short while before dusk - they rarely bothered with watches any more, but lived by the angle of the sun - they stopped in the middle of vast emptiness, and coaxed the petrol stove to cook behind a tarpaulin wind-break.

It was Daraprim night. After the anti-malarial tablets, Jim took the opportunity to do a health check. He had noticed some slackness about daily anti-fungal foot treatment, but commended their conscientious use of water-purification tablets (boiling water had become too tedious).

"By the way," said Jim, "one doesn't like to pry, but I haven't seen Andrew with a spade for several days now, indeed not since the Mount of Olives." Andrew agreed that being moved on at gunpoint by the Jordanian army seemed to have had a beneficial effect on dysentery. Just in case the psychological trauma had induced anything permanent, they scanned the medicine chest for constipation remedies, and discovered a bottle of liquid paraffin - to be used only as a threat.

"Right," said Andrew, "now how about you?"

"Ah, well, since you ask, I've got a bit of a rash," said Jim, "but it's probably only the heat." Ignoring his protests, they checked the manual. The majority verdict was chicken-pox, rated non-life-threatening with few after-effects if you didn't scratch. Since the other three had had chicken-pox as children, they were nonchalantly dismissive of the misery it caused to adults. All slept soundly in spite of the heavy lorries on the nearby road - until around dawn a donkey trotted past, whereupon everyone woke up.

Richard was complaining that Damascus four times in ten days was a bit much, as they turned West for Lebanon. The sun moved past noon while they climbed the coastal hills, and dipped towards evening as they snaked down the bumpy road to Beirut. The offices of Catoni & Co. were still open, so Abu Zeid's recommendation was mentioned, small cups of boiled coffee and sugar were consumed, and passage to Port Said was negotiated - a Greek ship leaving in four days' time.

The new-fangled jets roared their take-offs and landings at the airport across the road. The sun beat down on the sandy beach where Charlie was parked. The plastic soccer ball had burst and the sea was rough, but a sort of water polo had been devised, involving throwing the remains of the ball so the catcher had to jump just as a large wave broke over him. Not intellectually complex, but great fun.

July 31st. arrived - a full month since they left England. But the milestone brought no joy, only impatience. For a couple of days they had done little but swim and eat and sleep; they felt healthy and bronzed, and no one could explain why a sort of gloom should permeate the proceedings. But it did. Maybe it was because they had spent half of this first month driving in circles around Palestine, and now had only two months left. They decided to do something constructive instead of playing cards. So Jim and Richard went to Biblos, a few miles up the coast, to inspect that "haven of classical culture", as the guide book put it, "the oldest continuously-inhabited city in the world" - the fourth such they had come across in the past month. Andrew and David decided they had had enough culture, and wandered among the rubble and pot-holes of Beirut for the afternoon.

There seemed to be much building in progress, with no planning permission required. The result was a bit higgledy-piggledy, without any consistent architectural theme.

After supper a number of the local youths joined them to drink Coca-Cola, and practise their English. The expedition was thus instructed on the religious situation (Christian in the North and Moslem in the South), political system (votes could be sold for up to £25 in some elections) and local customs (arguments frequently settled with firearms). The conversation drifted round to British politics.

"Does your government do what the people want?" asked the locals.

"Well, our government thinks it is doing the best thing for most people, even if the people don't like it."

"If they don't like it, do the people get angry?"

"Yes, and a new government gets elected, which then does the same thing."

"But don't they have different parties?"

"Yes, Conservatives, who have the most able leaders, and Socialists, who have the best policies." There was not unanimity on either point. It was getting late, and they had to start early for the docks, so the meeting broke up, and the Expedition retired to sleeping bags alongside the Land Rover.

It was just before dawn that Jim heard whispering and metallic scratching in his hair-trigger sleep. He leapt to his feet, shouting. The others woke and scrabbled out of sandy sleeping bags. Jim was pursuing some one across the beach, shouting "Stop! Thief!" or something equally original. The others, on automatic pilot, followed. Then Andrew remembered he had no clothes on, so did a smart about turn. Richard joined Jim in leading the pursuit. A car engine started on the road nearby. Whoever it was was getting away with whatever they had taken. David, lying third at the time, ran back to the Land Rover. The doors were locked and it took a while to find the keys. Then Charlie leapt to life, bounded up the beach to the road, and set off after the disappearing car headlights.

Thoughts were jostling in David's brain. One was that Land Rovers didn't accelerate very well on Syrian petrol. Another was that he was alone, and whoever had robbed them probably wasn't, and a sort of anxious thought nudged to the front, asking what happened if he caught up with them. Charlie rounded a bend in the promenade, and there in the headlights was, oh joy, a police van. David jammed on the brakes and jumped out. What language was spoken in Lebanon? French?

"Vite! Nous sommes vollez! After them!" he cried.

The two policemen looked at each other, and yawned.

"Passport?" they asked.

Meanwhile, back on the beach, the growing light aided assessment of the damage. Most valuables were kept inside the Land Rover, but, of the bits and pieces outside, some pullovers, shoes, the Monopoly set and twenty pounds in travellers' cheques seemed missing. Andrew, now decent, was brewing coffee as Charlie and the police van arrived. The police, who had kept to the 25 mph speed limit all the way back, examined the scene of the crime. They then examined everyone's passport, and finally, as they left (without being offered coffee) they suggested that somebody should go the police-station, two kilometres away, and make a formal report. "Well, I ask you," was the most charitable of subsequent remarks.

One of the lads who sold Coca-Cola came along with David's address book, which had been found further along the beach. They dug around that area, and found most of the missing items loosely covered with sand. Sadly, one of the few things unrecovered was the pullover that Jim's Mum had knitted. They kicked themselves for having had some travellers' cheques out overnight, and thanked goodness that the rest were safely locked in the Land Rover, and that Jim had woken before the door of the cab had been forced. They ate a desultory breakfast while the morning's events were analysed. The consensus favoured a local job, probably some of the friendly youths who had chatted the previous evening. It left a nasty taste in the mouth.

An airmail letter was written to their bank-manager back home, cancelling the stolen travellers' cheques. There was little enthusiasm for visiting the local police again, and, besides, they had a boat to catch.

MS Lydia was the centre of a festival of chaotic officialdom. The Port Police issued forms, stamped them, then took them back. A large

Customs Man demanded an inventory of Charlie's contents; Richard told them it would take a week. A small Customs Man ordered the Land Rover to be emptied; Jim, towering above him, placed a heavy arm on his shoulder and smiled in a kindly way. Money-changers, porters, kebab-sellers, touted for business in the milling throng of passengers and crew. Noise and confusion ruled. Uniforms of various shades looked accusingly at passports, tickets, insurance documents, transit authorisations and visas. As if the congestion needed augmentation, bands of scruffy individuals appealed for cigarettes or backsheesh. The frenzy of arm-waving and paper-stamping lasted three hours before Charlie was slung aboard. Then, shortly after noon Lydia wallowed slowly out to sea.

"I was really getting to like the Lebanese before they robbed us," said Andrew next morning. The breeze was pleasantly cooling, but made the sea choppy; Lydia rolled about in a top-heavy way. They had slept on deck, with their wallets underneath them, and were now partaking of a leisurely breakfast. The crew had discouraged the lighting of stoves, but tinned sausages and tinned pilchards tasted fine when cold. The mixture of other passengers fascinated them: there were short plump Greeks with heavy suitcases, a few nuns of indeterminate origin, sallow Slavs who stood with backs to cabin walls, Arabs smoking pungent leaves, an American in dark glasses who spoke little, and even two Cambridge undergraduates with a Hillman Imp. It was like something out of a Graham Greene novel. A dour Scot and his equally dour girlfriend warned them earnestly against Egyptians; they claimed to have travelled through fifty countries, and had found none to equal Egypt for red tape, dishonesty, filth, incompetence, ...It made you wonder why they wanted to visit it again!

"Where's David?" asked Jim.

"He's being sick at the back of the boat," said Andrew. "He told me not to tell you."

In the midday haze Port Said came alongside. Loading at Beirut had taken three hours. Surely disembarkation would take less? It took five.

Chapter Six - Egypt

"It's a matter of principle. We will not give in to blackmail!" Andrew was adamant. They had already been sworn at for refusing to give the dockers "backsheesh", and they were not going to pay this greasy little man to "look after them" as he asked. The greasy little man shrugged and spat. They sat in the Port Said Customs Yard, and baked in the Land Rover. Other vehicles were constantly beckoned forwards to be inspected and released. Each time Jim started the engine and moved forward, an official of some sort would shout and shake his head and wave a sheaf of forms. The day dragged on.

Eventually Charlie sat alone, the last left. A uniform sauntered across with forms to be completed. Maybe he smiled or maybe he sneered, it could have been either. The forms had "Residents Returning from Overseas" at the top. "Sorry," said the man, "we've run out of the others." They filled them in; they paid for "visitors' number plates" to be attached front and back; they showed their passports for the umteenth time; they bit their tongues and refrained from comment. Another uniform appeared - they were to unpack the contents of the Land Rover. "But it took two days to pack!" exploded Richard, who had had enough.

"Why do you require this?" asked Jim, with the quiet authority of one used to dealing with non-commissioned officers. "We want to speak to your superior." The man hesitated, then walked away to an office.

"Sorry, David, but you'll have to get out the cigarettes," sighed Jim. He started the engine and drove towards the gateway. A couple of guards got to their feet.

"Do we give you these?" asked David, offering a couple of cartons through the window. The guards looked at each other, took the cartons, and raised the barrier.

"A pity, but we were getting short of time," agreed Andrew. They drove to find Damanhous, the shipping agents mentioned on Abu Zeid's documents. There was no fresh news of the Mokoto. It was due to arrive in about a week, they were told, so "telephone in a few days' time."

They followed signs for Cairo, partly because Richard's aunt was there, and partly because all tourists want to see the pyramids. On the outskirts of Port Said hunger overtook them, and they stopped to cook. The natives seemed friendly; indeed, the owner of the nearest house came over and showed them round his garden, insisting they accepted a large bunch of roses. As they were finishing supper a policeman came by, again very friendly, but evidently concerned lest they were thinking of staying. He looked up and down the quiet road basking in the evening warmth, and, lowering his voice, urged them to drive on - "for your lives" he said.

"A bit melodramatic, don't you think?" asked Richard, as they headed towards Ismailia.

"Don't forget," replied Jim "that the British invaded and occupied this place eight years ago, so I doubt if we are much loved."

The desert mice made little scampering noises around Charlie and climbed over Andrew's feet. Apart from that, the sand dunes were silent beneath a huge starry sky. Andrew was taking the first watch, from ten to midnight; he sat with his back to a wheel, the expedition's crowbar across his knees - it was their nearest thing to a weapon. Egypt's reputation made it essential that someone stayed awake, even though they had camped well past the houses of Ismailia and quarter of a mile from the road. Other groups' harrowing tales of tents and wheels and wallets removed overnight made them determined to stay alert. But wasn't the desert beautiful? So many stars! A sudden loud shout almost stopped Andrew's heart. He leapt to his feet and turned on the lamp. But it was only one of the others having a bad dream. Everyone sat up for a minute, and, since it was about midnight, Richard took over the watch. Soon the sleeping bags were breathing regularly again.

Moths and mosquitoes and other insects were pinging against the lamp glass; Richard was about to turn it off, but thought he might fall asleep if it was dark. He yawned, got up and walked around Charlie. All was terribly quiet, the sort of silence you couldn't get in England, where was always the distant sound of a dog or an engine or a stream. He tried to keep alert by making his mind go over everything that had happened during the day. He hated having to bribe people; but maybe, he then thought, it's the same as tipping. The only difference, really, between bribes and tips is the timing of the gift - before instead of afterwards. Not that he really approved of tipping either - a bit patronising. The silence was oppressive. What else had happened today? They had had an argument about the Beatles; Andrew had admitted liking their music, and the others had laughingly accused him of being trendy, currying favour with the masses! Surely no mature adult could seriously enjoy such noise! Now, Lilacs in the Spring, A Policeman's Lot, If you were the Only Girl in the World - that was real music! Richard yawned again, and listened to the silence. He wished he could play the piano. They had sometimes cycled out to fenny pubs in magical villages like Wilbraham and Shelford, where, after a pint, Edward - another Emmanuel oarsman - could turn woodwormed uprights into Bechstein grands! Everyone would roar out the old favourites in glorious harmony - at least that's what it sounded like to the singers. Then their bicycles would weave slowly home beneath the bronze evening sky. Some said that you needed hills to think against, but to him flat East Anglia was England...... Why had he signed on for three years in Northern Rhodesia?

The way to really see a city is to get lost in it. This the Expedition managed to do quite well as they looked for Richard's aunt. In parts, Cairo was more Eastern than Amman, and in other parts more Western than Beirut. And much bigger than either. The overwhelming memory that would linger was of a frightening volume of people. As they drove through squalid backstreets reeking of hopeless poverty they were running out of adjectives to express their feelings.

"At least British slums have a dimension that makes it reasonable to tackle the problem," said Richard. "And don't say that education is the answer here! Where would you start? The thought buckles the imagination."

Then they found themselves in tree-lined avenues along the Nile, where graceful feluccas arched their sails, and shoals of expensive cars swept round sparkling hotels - a world thousands of years away from the mat-and-box shacks in the alleys of wretchedness.

"How does Abdel Nasser impose a semblance of order on this

place?" asked David. "How do you rule a mixture of border-line survival and stifling superfluity so that both ends of the spectrum support you? I'm starting to get a sneaking respect for the man."

They stopped frequently to ask about the CMS Hospital. Those they approached were of two sorts, either professing no knowledge whatsoever of English, (or French, or German,) or else terribly helpful, knowing just where it was and giving explicit directions, which were entirely wrong. Maybe both varieties were anxious not to spend too long talking to an English Land Rover.

The suspicion that not everyone loved them was strengthened when Charlie got incredibly wedged in some sort of market. Trying to find their way out of a primeval network of murky lanes, they had tried what looked like a short cut down a narrow street, which became full of stalls and people and camels. "Nature abhors a vacuum," muttered Andrew, as any temporary space in front of them quickly filled with teeming humanity. Charlie nosed gently through the throng of gowns and robes, until suddenly there was a wall in front of them. Then the fun really started! Somehow they had to turn round without knocking over too much of the surroundings. It was when the front bumper was tight against a fruit-stall and the back bumper made contact with a donkey cart that they got really worried.

"There are lots of people in pyjamas waving their fists at us," reported Richard from the back. "Can you move ahead?"

"No," said Andrew tersely. "Can you get out and guide me back?" At this point the crowd started banging on the sides of the Land Rover.

"I am definitely not getting out," said Richard firmly. "Try easing back a little - the donkey has moved a bit." Like a tortoise in a toast-rack Charlie inched to and fro, while more and more people crowded round. In desperation, Andrew used the klaxon, which had two effects: it annoyed the crowd, who shouted things, and stimulated the donkey into shooting forward into a purveyor of brass trays.

"You can go back a couple of feet if you're quick," called Richard. A perspiring Andrew did, saying to himself "and if the large lady in a sheet would stand somewhere else I could almost get past the melons." They chuntered backwards and forwards for what seemed minutes on end, while the noise around them grew to a crescendo.

"I say," came Richard's pained voice, "they're throwing things!" A volley of vegetables thundered on the metal roof. "Do you think they know we're British?"

"Keep going, Andrew; you're nearly round!" David encouraged, trying not to sound panicky.

"We must defuse the situation. Smile and wave!" ordered Jim. With waggling fingers, like demented royalty, they leered with fixed grins at the seething mob, which didn't seem particularly defused. Suddenly a gap in the crowd opened for a moment, and Charlie dived for it like a homing rabbit. Followed by a parting sally of splattering melon slices and tomatoes, they sped down the street to freedom. It had very nearly been very unpleasant.

They resumed their search, criss-crossing the city with stops to ask directions. They now tried selecting only pedestrians who looked intelligent, and were encouraged that every one knew the words "left" and "right". However, it appeared that either the words meant something else or their users had a subtle sense of humour. It took three hours to reach the hospital.

Richard's aunt was exactly what a hospital matron should be - solid, sensible and very kind. She had spent years ministering to Belhazia cases. Belhazia, or, more technically, Schistosomyesis, was a parasite which infected eighty percent of the population, apparently. Anaemia and stomach upsets were the symptoms caused by the worms eating away at liver and intestines. A three-weeks course of injections could cure a sufferer, but, as the matron said "they go straight back to working thigh-deep in water, and pick it up again."

The cold orange-juice she provided was bliss after the stress of the trans-Cairo journey - no one dared ask if it was safe to drink! The dear lady asked where they were staying, and, on hearing that they hadn't found a site yet, suggested they tried All Saints' Cathedral, whose caretaker she knew. The Anglican Bishop had been expelled by Nasser some years before, mainly for being deliberately British.

When they reached All Saints, the caretaker, to their amazement, said that it would be nice to have the Bishop's flat used again. So for the first time in over a month the Expedition found a roof overhead - and what a roof! The Bishop's Residence had about a dozen large rooms, broad balconies, two 'fridges and two showers - and Cambridge to Capetown 1964 made hay while the sun shone.

Late that evening, really clean for the first time in weeks, they felt like nineteenth century plantation-owners as they sat playing bridge in the spacious sitting-room. It was nearly midnight, very late by their standards, but there would be no guard rota tonight in the tense shadowy hours. Charlie was safely locked up below their window in the Cathedral yard, and the Cathedral yard had a big locked gate. Just to be sure, the spare wheels had been removed from the Land Rover's bonnet and back door, and the spare springs removed from the roof-rack. They were not risking anything in Egypt.

"Oh frabjous day! Callooh! Callay!" yawned Jim, stretching for another cup of coffee. "But these expeditions are gruelling!"

"Does anyone else feel a mite guilty about living in luxury?" asked Andrew. Nobody appeared particularly stricken, but David did say that his grandmother's favourite saying was "All this laughing will come to crying!"

"What are we doing tomorrow?" asked Richard.

What they were doing tomorrow started with the Cathedral Communion, just downstairs and across the yard. Then they were invited to a Parish Breakfast - a real English one! They sat near the Archdeacon, who possessed two gold teeth and a strong pride in belonging to original Egyptian stock. He told them that the Anglicans had only six clergy in the country, but that other churches, particularly the Coptic, were much stronger. "In our population of twenty-five million there are maybe eight million Christians. We used to be a Christian country, but with increasing number of Arabs there are now more mosques than churches."

After breakfast they went to be "registered" with the local police, as regulations required. Then they serviced the Land Rover. It was getting so hot by lunchtime that they retired to the large armchairs in the large lounge and dozed like toads in teacups. Nor did they exert themselves before early evening, when there was a "Son et Lumiere" at the pyramids, to which they drove, feeling uncomfortably like tourists.

The Sphinx was much smaller than they had expected, but it looked quite magical when lit by green and yellow spotlights. The suave recorded voices of English actors narrated the story of Egyptian civilisation, while the pyramid of Cheops which had taken a hundred thousand workers fifty years to build, towered in massive symmetry against the apricot sky. No stage could have had a more awesome backdrop. And yet, and yet, to live up to their expectation it should have been much bigger! When your imagination has been fed all your life with tales of the greatest wonder of the ancient world, the physical reality is bound to be something of an anticlimax.

August 6th. There might be some word of the Mokoto. Jim phoned the Port Said Agents: It took two hours to get a free line, and then there was no definite news - maybe tomorrow.

Fresh vegetables seemed a good idea. If you didn't know where the nearest market was, the obvious thing to do was to enquire at the Hilton Hotel. Maybe they looked too scruffy, for Richard got the raised eyebrow and blank unhelpfulness. David, equally scruffy, then had the idea of going in and putting on an American accent; "I gotta kinda cravin' for tomaytoes I guess! Can you guys tell me where to buy some?" Immediately three clerks competed to produce maps, fluttering around, pointing directions. Interesting.

They had learnt to say "mish mumpkin", the Arabic for "impossible", and used it to good effect in bargaining for tomatoes:

"Five piastres a kilo is far too much, why that's about a shilling! Mish mumpkin! How about three?"

"May my mother be saved from destitution! Four piastres, then."

"OK," said David smugly, paying up. Richard shook his head about this over-eagerness. He went to another stall, where again tomatoes were five piastres a kilo:

"Mish mumpkin!" exclaimed Richard indignantly. "I'll give you two."

"For you, special price, four piastres," said the shopkeeper after bewailing the harshness of the visiting Excellencies.

"Two," said Richard.

"Four is best price!"

"May your grandmother be anointed with goat-droppings! Come," he gestured grandly to the others, "let us depart this

trically away. A shout followed them:
ill starve, but three piastres!"
You see," he explained afterwards,
for being a bit rough on the chap's
to go through the procedure - it's expected
urse the others had to compete at neighbouring
d up with an awful lot of tomatoes.
S Hospital was within walking distance, so they
nt to the matron, hoping she liked tomatoes!

The hospital was pretty basic by British standards, but did a great job for its patients. "We used to take a thousand at a time," said Richard's aunt, "but a government inspection three years ago insisted that we provided beds to lie on, and tables for meals, so we have space for only four hundred now." She produced mid-morning tea with, oh joy, the first fruit-cake since England. The luxury of fruit-cake made them realise they had been getting used to being really hungry. It was a sobering thought that most people round about must have been a great deal hungrier - and not just occasionally.

The hospital errand-boys took them to see some Coptic churches. One was the famous "hanging church", built between two walls of a Roman fort; another was on the supposed site of the Holy Family's sojourn in Egypt (although the Expedition's theology division questioned the historical accuracy - saying that the single New Testament reference may have been to echo Old Testament prophecies). Both churches were exquisitely decorated with intricate panelling of ivory and ebony. For sheer magnificence it was, David remarked, in its own way on a level with fruit-cake.

Returning, they met an Islamic funeral procession in a narrow sewerage-swilled alley, and pressed into a doorway as the wailing mourners went past. The lads from the hospital got sworn at for being in the company of the British. It was all a bit uncomfortable. Andrew, quite out of character, was moved to anger, loudly expressing his opinion of Egypt in terms of stench, improbity, and mendacity. Just in case any bystander had a dictionary, he was quickly hurried away, still muttering darkly behind his spectacles.

Their mail had got through to Cairo. Jim sat reading, and

rereading, three letters from Sal, impervious to the heat of late afternoon and the cynical envy of the others. The telephonic services were less efficient than the postal; Richard had spent most of the day trying to phone Port Said, but the lines were out of action. They worried in case the Mokoto had arrived, although it was not due for another four days.

David had spent the day at the embassies of Nigeria and Ghana, whose London branches had been either unwilling or unable to complete the paperwork before they left the UK. The Nigerian Embassy in Cairo was, in terms of lethargy and incompetance, on a level with London; after waiting for an hour David had been told that he might need a visitor's visa, but the visa official was away somewhere and no one was sure when he would be back - "maybe in a few days". The Ghanaian embassy had been much more helpful, and even gave him a copy of an Accra newspaper, almost entirely dedicated to praising President Kwame Nkrumah.

The others had been to the Cairo museum, and were still raving about golden tombs, fabulous jewels, indescribably beautiful ornaments and mummies galore. Some one had bought a two-day old Times on the way back, and they now devoured every word in a feeding frenzy for English news.

"Tomorrow and tomorrow and tomorrow creeps in this petty pace," sighed Andrew. The hot days had followed each other with no news from Port Said. The shipping agents would evidently be notified of the Mokoto's approach only a day before she arrived, and they expected her to stay only a few hours. The worrying thing was that telephones worked only intermittently. The Expedition, unwilling to take any risk of missing the boat, decided to be at Port Said two days early, just in case. Besides, they were getting fed up of Cairo. The comfort of the Bishop's House merely aggravated their impatience; they had built up expectations of three months hardship, or at least intrepid effort, and idle relaxation did nothing for their self-esteem.

So tomorrow they would leave. The morning had been spent cleaning the house from top to bottom, so that no bishop would even suspect they had been there. After lunch, in that drowsy time of day when all but mad dogs and Englishmen sleep, they played bridge.

Emma VI – 1963

Jim, Richard, Andrew and Charlie – Clean and New

Richard and David – Week One

Loading at Suez

Richard, David, Flaky Pastry Chef, Claude and another of Mokoto's crew

Richard and Jim on Red Sea

Not thinking what's in the hold

Irish Company – 5th King's S.A. Rifles 1916

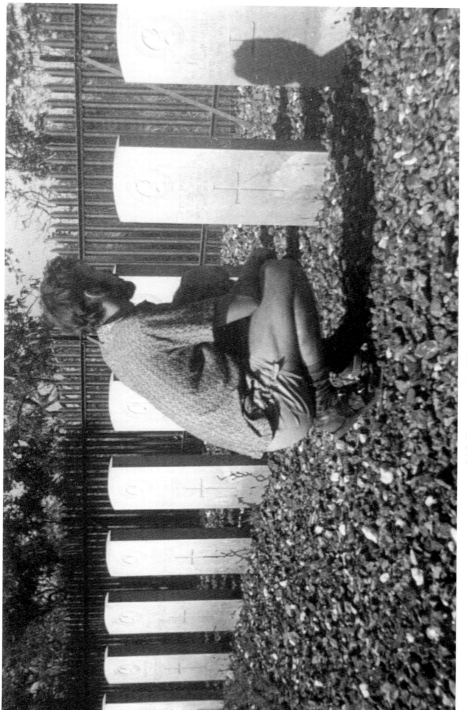

Irish Company – 5th King's S.A. Rifles 1964

At Ituk Mban at last

Richard made seven no trumps, doubled and redoubled, a lifetime first. But their hearts were not in it. Bridge was too redolent of a leisurely colonial way of life. What else could they do to fill the gaping afternoon? All the things good tourists do had been done: Ptolemaic marvels had been admired and Memphis had been visited. What else was there? It was too hot to walk far, and they didn't really want to take Charlie out again. The Land Rover was loaded for departure in the morning, snug and safe in the yard, not to be exposed unnecessarily to Egyptian traffic.

Someone found the monopoly set.

Five hours later Andrew landed on a hotel-ridden Mayfair. The rent was astronomic. "I'm finished!" said Andrew.

"No, you're not, if David accepts Marylebone instead," said Richard.

"Sorry, I need more than that," said David.

"Come on," said Jim, "else Andrew is out."

"Winning is the object of the game," protested David.

"That's a typical capitalist slogan," said Jim, "let the poor perish! Let the rich get richer!"

"It's a game!" sulked David. "There is no point in playing if nobody loses!"

"That's a pretty mean attitude....." Richard was snapping, as the caretaker came in with a telegram from the shipping agent - "Mokoto due tonight. Load tomorrow noon."

They left before seven in the morning. The hundred and fifty miles to Port Said would take little over three hours, but they wanted to leave enough time to find the way out of Cairo; this was sensible since the rare signpost they found was written in Arabic. Once past the airport on the Ismailia road, driving was a joy - you hardly moved the steering wheel for miles, so straight was the road over the gently rolling desert. The sand looked like almond paste in the early sun. Further on, they drove through huge dunes which could have passed for brown sugar. Sweetness permeated the Expedition's mood as well, for there was a feeling that at last they were on the way to Africa proper. They reached Port Said well before noon, and went straight to Damanhous for instructions.

There they were greeted by a certain amount of embarrassed foot shuffling. "Ah, we tried to 'phone you last night," said a senior clerk, "because there has been a snag......... The Mokoto could not dock, so has left."

In Winnie-the-Pooh there is a story in which Piglet trips up while carrying a large balloon, which bursts. Piglet then spends some time wondering whether the world has blown up, or just his bit of it. If, at that moment in Port Said, any member of the Expedition had been asked, he would have said that he knew exactly how Piglet felt. After a period of silence all four spoke simultaneously:

"LEFT?"

"On through the canal. They would not let her near the port."

"Why not?"

"We were not aware of the Mokoto's cargo until yesterday."

"Which was?"

"She is carrying consignments for the copper mines in Northern Rhodesia."

"Consignments?"

"Of explosives...........the Port Authorities would not give permission to approach the docks." There was a considerable pause.

"So what about us?"

There was a certain amount of shrugging together with a modicum of sympathy, but it became obvious that Cambridge to Capetown 1964 was expendable. No, there was no other ship available for some weeks. He could not begin to say how much they regretted the situation. Jim produced the tickets, and looked at them.

"These tickets make the Compagnie Maritime de Belge legally responsible for getting us to Mombasa. We will of course sue them, and their agents, for very heavy damages due to unfulfilled commitments and loss of reputation."

"Let me find the Manager," said the unhappy clerk hastily.

There was much agitated discussion sotto voce from the adjoining room before the Manager appeared. Maybe he always looked anxious, but he was certainly looking anxious now. Yes, he wanted to help all he could, but events were not under his control. However, he would wire the captain immediately and request him to stop at Port Suez to load the Land Rover.

"If he won't, we must cable Antwerp immediately and insist the owners honour their obligations," said Richard. "Can you give us their telegraphic address?" The Manager held up both hands, shaking his head. "Wait there a moment, please," he smiled nervously, and disappeared next door. The four were left alone, and collapsed onto chairs, feeling utterly spent.

"That was brilliant, Jim!" murmured David. "Thank heavens you came up with that legal stuff. Where did you learn all that?"

"Nowhere," admitted Jim modestly, "I haven't a clue about legal obligations." The others wished he hadn't told them that. The Manager returned with clerks hovering behind, and the Expedition held its collective breath.

"You have your ticket, so the captain must stop. We will tell him to anchor off Suez when he gets through the canal, because you have your ticket. So he must. Now you must get to Suez and contact our office there."

They thanked him effusively, and Charlie was soon hurrying along the road by the canal. It was certainly well guarded; every few hundred yards an Egyptian sentry was stationed, maybe to guard against another English attack? The road wasn't wide but there was very little traffic, so they made good time. Occasionally they would meet or overtake a row of ships. It was strange to see a liner protruding over a sand dune, or to have a giant tanker towering over them. They wondered how far along the Mokoto had got, but did not sight anything with such a name. They reached Suez early in the evening and found the Damanhous office. Everyone was gathered round the radio, listening to a speech by Nasser. There was no need to rush, they were told; arrangements for loading would be made the next day when the Mokoto emerged from the canal. No, they could not say what time

No matter, the expedition would be ready. There was an open square near the Damanhous office, dotted with welcome trees, which seemed suitable for their last night in Egypt. Small groups of locals were gathered round radios, listening to the third or fourth hour of Nasser's oration. The Expedition placed a large tarpaulin on the sandy ground to denote its sphere of influence, and began the evening's cooking. Fifty or sixty children congregated to watch proceedings.

Concerned lest they burn themselves on the stove (or, more likely, lest the stove disappear), Richard would patrol the edge of the tarpaulin, growling, when the onlookers pressed too close. Sometimes the infant crowd grew too bold, and you would find a small head peering into a saucepan or a small grubby hand prodding you in the back with "Hello. Hello," or "Hey, you, speak English?" David, grinding his teeth, urged self-restraint lest the image of the Raj be tarnished - particularly since they had to spend the night there. Richard, much as he itched to cuff the odd ear-hole, confined himself to an occasional leaping to the feet with a snarling roar, which would cause the throng to temporarily retreat in disarray. Andrew observed that Richard would make a very good teacher, being endowed with a fierce exterior and a soft heart. Eventually adults appeared and rounded up the offspring. Either it was bedtime or Nasser had finished broadcasting for the day.

It was warm and peaceful in the half light; in the distance was the soft swish of great ships gliding into the Gulf of Suez and the buzz of attendant launches carrying pilots to and fro. An elderly Egyptian soldier patrolling their area came across to chat.

"Where you come from?"

"England."

"No. Not England."

"Yes, we all come from the British Isles."

"America?"

"No."

"Germany?"

"No, England. We are English. Really." In sweaty shirts, scruffy shorts and disintegrating sandals, they did not feel a particularly glowing advert for any country. Maybe the old soldier expected the English to be better dressed.

"Anthony Eden?" he asked dubiously.

"Retired," they told him. There was thoughtful pause.

"Abdul Nasser good, yes?" That was a bit tricky, but being sure that Nasser must have had more than average ability and ruthlessness to stay at the top so long, they felt justified in assuring him that they thought Abdul Nasser was a great politician.

All was silent save for a crunching noise. The emaciated cats that hung around under the street lamps were catching and chewing moths. David was doing the four to six watch - having survived ten days in Egypt without serious mishap, they were not going to risk anything in the last furlong and had each done their two hours duty. A dull rainbow glow in the East was extinguishing the nearby stars as David lit the stove to make porridge. A dozen cats rose from their lean haunches and slunk away into the side streets. The sky was turning to warm peach as the sleeping bags stirred and muttered.

Jussef from Damanhous arrived as they were packing up. They just had time to buy six dozen postcards and seven kilograms of pears for the boat, before he guided them to the Customs Shed. There seemed nobody else leaving at the time, so the entire staff of police and customs concentrated on the Expedition. Every form was double-checked and each official stamp was examined suspiciously, while Jussef anxiously urged them to hurry since the Master of the Mokoto was already annoyed at having to wait. To speed things up they swallowed their scruples and tipped liberally, thus avoiding having to unpack Charlie. The Chief Inspecting Officer then wanted to know the engine serial number. Richard whispered desperately from under the bonnet that he couldn't find it under the caking of mud and dust. "What was that?" said the Inspector. Fortunately, David, standing slightly behind the official, could see over his shoulder. "My friend said...", and David read out the string of numbers from the form. "Yes, that agrees with the entry form," nodded the Inspector, a bit disappointed.

"Now we need the twenty five pounds embarkation fee," announced a customs officer. Consternation; they had not heard about this before. Jim negotiated and finally agreed to ten pounds. "Now all we need is your payment of three pounds each to leave the country." Andrew was beginning to express his opinion of Egypt and its inhabitants again, so they quickly paid up, before someone thought of another charge. Port Suez was getting very expensive.

Out at last in the heat of early afternoon, they drove along the quay to a lighter. A rusty crane, embossed with the word Ipswich, was nursed into life and the Land Rover was swung into the air at an alarming angle. "This not the first time I am loading," pouted the driver, offended by their shouts. He accepted a carton of cigarettes and gently lowered Charlie onto the barge. They then sat and waited for an hour or two, until a tug appeared. It was a small tug with a large crew. The crew were very friendly and insisted on giving a guided tour of their engine room, but showed no urgent inclination to actually tow them anywhere. Eventually it became clear that some inducement was customary, and in weary desperation cartons of cigarettes were distributed.

"You our friends. You write us letter from England. We brothers," laughed the crew. The tug set off across the bay to a rather graceful merchant ship, and the Mokoto's derricks hoisted them aboard. It had been a long day.

Chapter Seven - The Mokoto

Mokoto's engines throbbed into life and she nosed out into the Red Sea in the twilight. Charlie was roped down on deck, surrounded by its four travelling companions. The First Officer, down from the bridge to inspect the new arrivals, enquired (in French) how his deck cargo intended feeding themselves for the ten days it would take to reach Mombasa. He hastened to rule out any thought of using a petrol stove on top of holds full of explosives. Instead, he said with a weary sigh, he would ask the Chef if the Expedition might use the ship's galley occasionally. He gave the unmistakable impression that his two-legged deck cargo was a confounded nuisance. Monsieur Le Chef, tall and bearded, resplendent in a tall white hat, seemed to agree. Presiding over the large modern kitchen, a short fat pastry-chef scowling at his elbow, Jean Marie gave a Gallic shrug and frowningly said that tomorrow at 8.30 am and 6.30 p.m. *les garcons* could use the facilities. He did not say what fate awaited them if anything was out of place afterwards. The *garcons* found themselves back on deck, feeling like tramps at the back door of the Ritz.

They unrolled their sleeping bags on the metal deck, and lay looking at the stars. It had been a very long and very wearisome day, but at least they were free of Egypt. It was said that Nasser had given instructions to boost tourism and welcome visitors, but the message had clearly not yet reached the port authorities. There was agreement that Egypt would not be high on their agenda for further visits. They watched the dim lights of Suez fade behind them

"I'd love a cigarette!" said David.

"Not while we are living on top of this cargo!" Andrew reminded him.

"Besides," said Jim casually, "the tug crew got the last of them, remember?"

"I don't think they can be good for you anyway," said Richard, in a comforting sort of voice. There were footsteps on the stairs leading down from the galley and Jean Marie appeared with a large plate of pork chops.

"Left over," he shrugged, "if you don't eat them they go *aux poissons*, to the fishes."

For three days the Mokoto churned steadily down the Red Sea at fourteen knots, the hot blue sky above and the calm blue sea around. Each evening at 6.30 when they arrived at the kitchen, there would happen to be four huge helpings left over, to be saved from *les poissons*. Once again the world was conspiring to prevent the Expedition living rough - not that there were any complaints from the Expedition. Shipboard life was pretty immobile, but nobody felt like being particularly mobile when you became sweat-soaked merely by climbing the stairs to the kitchen. Spirits were high, for, with the distance to Africa proper shortening by the hour, they no longer felt they were helplessly waiting.

"I didn't realise the Red Sea was so long," said David after supper on the third day. They were taking coffee in the petty officers' mess after a frugal snack of soup, steak and chips, ice-cream and flaky pastries.

"Tomorrow," said Claude, the Second Engineer, "we reach the Gulf of Aden - the Red Sea is *presque finis*, over." All the sailors seemed to speak English at least as well as the Expedition spoke French, so conversation was carried on in the other's language with insertions of a word in one's own when stuck.

Lucienne, the helmsman, wanted to know what Cambridge University food was like. "*Pas aussi bon que le votre!*" David assured him, and the flaky pastry chef beamed with pleasure.

"And you wear dinner jackets each *soir, oui*? Like in the film I see about undergraduates?"

"*Non, pas* dinner jackets, *mais nous devons portez* gowns *chaque soir*," said Andrew. Yes, grace was said in Latin. No, not at breakfast. No, it wasn't an outdated bastion of privilege. Well, yes, they were waited on by menservants at dinner - like old George, whose thick-lensed spectacles were a mere fashion accessory; *inutile c'est a dire*; well, he was nearly blind - he would dip his hand into your soup to see if you had finished. No, they weren't joking - really! Well, he had been there for over sixty years, and there was such a thing as reciprocal loyalty - now, that took some translating! Faithfulness on both sides?

"So men serve the food! Are there no women?"

"*Seulement* bed-makers - only for *arranger les lits*."

"But is not that a temptation for the hot blooded British youth, yes?" grinned Jean Marie. "Oh yes, women in the bedroom!"

"*Non, non, non!*" exclaimed David. "*Nous avons un regulation tres ancient qui dit que les* 'Bed-makers must be Neither Young nor Comely'!"

"Comely?"

"*Belle, peut etre - ni jeune, ni belle*. What's the French word for Sexy?"

"*Oui, oui,* I understand. But you have girl friends, yes? Are they not permitted to visit?"

"*Seulement avant de dix heurs du soir,*" replied Andrew.

"So all immorality over by ten?" winked Claude. Andrew sprang to the defence of the College's good name, insisting that no good Emma man was immoral before ten o'clock at night, which for some reason caused general mirth.

"It seems" said the ship's electrician, wiping his eyes, "that your college *c'est comme* Mokoto, you go out for the women!"

"Wait 'til we arrive Mombasa," broke in the pastry chef, "we take you find black girls that screw like rabbits! You like that, Andrew?" Andrew cleaned his glasses with studied concentration, and said he thought perhaps not, but it was kind of them to offer.

Next morning found Mokoto passing through the narrow straits at the Southern end of the Red Sea and swinging due East for the horn of Africa. Perim Island lay astern on the Port side and Djibouti somewhere in the distance to Starboard. The Expedition leaned on the rail. A black fin sliced through the water ahead, the first shark they had seen. There was a fresher wind this morning - a pleasant change after the steam-bath conditions of the last couple of days. The First Officer joined the group to say that they might feel the tail of the monsoon season as they moved into the Indian Ocean, and that the Captain (who remained a distant figure on the bridge) would allow them to use the spare cabins rather than have them exposed on deck. Andrew, in stoic mood, pointed out that the air-conditioning below, not to mention the bunks and showers, might mar their acclimatisation to African conditions; then, realising he was now alone on deck, he sportingly submitted to the majority view.

Mokoto's eleven thousand tonnes were rolling slightly in the increasing swell that evening, but not enough to detract from the Chef's five-course supper - the black sausages and rhubarb sauce were particularly memorable. The crew removed the canvas awnings from the deck next morning, fastened wooden blocks against Charlie's wheels, and tied extra ropes around stacked casks of acid. Richard asked why these were stored on deck: "Would you prefer them in the hold with the explosives?" was the reply. Further cheerful news was that worsening conditions were forecast, with thirty foot waves expected around Cape Guardafui, the tip of the horn. The Expedition's apprehension was not helped by the appearance of an increasing number of sharks, but no one cared to mention this omen. The crew, however, seemed quite cheerful living with a cargo of dynamite and acid - but then, they were being paid an extra fifteen percent "danger money". Jean Marie sang to himself in the kitchen as he prepared a special meal for the evening - it was a Belgian national holiday. Outside, the wind was strengthening.

By late afternoon Mokoto was slithering down long waves, and David gave his apologies and retired below. The other three, smiling bravely, arrived promptly for the soup, which was excellent, as were the roast beef and potato rolls. When the fish and tomato pie arrived, Jim made his excuses and left quite suddenly. During the apple tart Richard noticed that Andrew was no longer with them either.

Three quarters of the Expedition slept, on and off, for thirty six hours. Occasionally, when there was a lurch of greater force than usual, they would wake and wonder if the explosives in the hold felt that one, then quickly try to sleep again. The wind never, thank goodness, became a full storm; but the ship moved about in quite a lively fashion and the Captain reduced speed to soften the impact of the waves.

Two days later hunger, and the smell of goulash and chips, tempted David and Jim to reappear for supper. Richard told them, rather smugly they thought, that they had missed superb kingclip steaks and lamb cutlets the previous night. The chefs found the *garcons'* discomfort in heavy weather highly amusing, and Jim and David pretended to join in the sociable mirth.

Andrew surfaced the next day, in time to celebrate crossing the Equator somewhere South of Mogadishu. The celebrations were genteel, consisting of mugs of tea and taking photographs - far more adult, they felt, than the silly nonsense of dressing up as Neptune and suchlike, so beloved by navies and tourists. Mokoto was still shouldering moderate seas as she headed South-west, parallel to the Somalia coast hidden in the distance. Although the wind was fairly strong, the sun shone, and the Expedition reclined on top of the hatches, no longer thinking of the cargo beneath.

"So, what's the programme after Mombasa?" asked Richard.

"Nairobi first," said David. "Our contacts are concentrated in large centres so that we can see several people in short time, but also because it's the large centres that have the large numbers of children needing teaching. If the new method can help solve the teacher shortage in the towns, it has helped solve the teacher shortage in the country."

"Sounds slick," said Andrew dubiously. "And after Nairobi?"

"We head on South. A couple of towns in Tanganyika, then the Northern Rhodesian copper belt and Lusaka, which isn't far from Richard's school - when does your term start at St. Mark's?"

"Second week in September."

"We should manage that OK.," nodded Jim, "leaving three weeks to do Southern Rhodesia and South Africa before Andrew and I fly back." It sounded simple.

They dozed in the hot and hazy sunshine. Another day or so would take them to Mombasa. After that there would be little time to lie around.

Mokoto circled very slowly outside Mombasa harbour as night fell. They had sighted the first land for five days earlier that afternoon, but couldn't reach port before dusk, and the Harbour Authority would not allow their cargo through the reefs and lagoons until dawn. Supper was strangely subdued. The Expedition was now impatient to get on the road again, but Mokoto had become home, and they could not light-heartedly leave. Jean Marie had cooked a huge ham which exhaled aromas of spice and herbs, but they had little appetite.

"It'll take you ages to finish this off!" Jim told him.

"*Non*, it will take <u>you</u> ages to finish," smiled Jean, "for tomorrow you take it with you!"

Charlie was packed and waiting at five-thirty the next morning. The pilot came aboard before six, and Mokoto nosed cautiously through the reef as the first flush of dawn coloured the thick vegetation above the line of white, white sand. So this was Africa! It felt very different somehow - different from Europe or Egypt, and a world away from English vicarages, thought Andrew. There was a loud clatter as the anchor dropped into the quiet water of the bay. Come on, come on, we want to get ashore, David worried to himself. Launches drew alongside. Immigration paperwork was completed in the Captain's cabin. The four passengers were rather surprised to see that their passport photos showed pale clean-shaven young men - that had been a long time ago.

The ship's Agent smiled patiently and said that Mokoto would be unloading most of its cargo onto barges before being allowed to dock - maybe in four or five days time. He calmed their loud concern. No, they would be unloaded today - in fact they could come ashore in his launch now, and he had a lighter on the way for the Land Rover.

Three thousand miles in Mokoto had made them feel part of a family, and parting was not easy. Addresses were exchanged, with exhortations to keep in touch. The Agent was waiting, and haste made the goodbyes less awkward, but it was with real sadness that they waved to the diminishing figures at the ship's rail.

"This is better than Egypt," smiled Richard, ducking the spray as they headed for the wharf, "we get ashore without having to bribe anyone - service without baksheesh! We knew that a Commonwealth country would be civilised and efficient!" The Agent frowned. "Newly independent countries have teething problems," he sighed. They wondered what he meant.

It was pleasant lying in the sunshine outside the row of customs sheds. They noticed that the ground seemed to roll slightly when they stood up to see if the barge from Mokoto was coming. Charlie arrived ashore at noon, and they could see it outside a customs shed some distance away. But when they went to collect it, the African customs officials in smart new uniforms said it could not be moved without "clearance". Andrew muttered something about "shades of Port

Said". At least the telephones worked better than the Egyptian ones, and Jim explained the problem to their shipping agents, who were very helpful, but couldn't find the right papers. David said he would be at their office directly, and a kind customs official of Indian origin drove him there - by which time the papers had been found and taken to the docks. David phoned Jim to say all was well. Jim said that it wasn't, because no papers had arrived. Meanwhile, Richard and Andrew had been looking round some of the other customs sheds, and, to their delight, came across an official with the papers for the Land Rover. He explained that the vehicle would have to be brought round to his section of the docks to be inspected, which sounded fairly straightforward, and when David arrived back, Richard had gone to collect it. However, Richard returned to say that for some reason the other customs officers would not let it be moved. The official with Charlie's papers scowled and spoke to a soldier on duty at the gate.

"There is some misunderstanding," he told them. "This Askari will go with you to explain things to them. Take your rifle." The last remark was addressed to the soldier, who saluted and accompanied Richard back down the docks.

It appeared that the Askari (and his rifle) was able to resolve the demarcation dispute, for Richard was soon back, driving Charlie. "It started second go," he announced proudly, "and after ten days of salt spray!"

"Now," they were told, "you will please empty the vehicle for inspection." Protests were of no avail, for this particular customs shed went by the rule book. The entire contents of Charlie were rowed out on the ground, and, although not one box or case was opened, each object (even the white punctured soccer ball) was marked with a piece of white chalk. While this inspection went on, they shared a spoon and a tin of pilchards. It seemed that pilchards had a certain soothing property, for when they were told that they could reload the boxes and tins, the tools and spare parts, the sleeping-bags, and tents, and all the other items marked with nice white chalk-marks, they smiled politely and said thank-you.

Chapter Eight - Kenya

Sitting in the Land Rover again was sort of comforting, like coming home to a favourite sofa. The flowering trees and lushness of Mombasa were giving way to scrub and bush which hemmed in the road and the railway line alongside, like antibodies attacking foreign organisms. Charlie seemed to like the place, and hummed smoothly to itself as the tarmac road sped by beneath. There was no hurry, since this was Friday, so they wouldn't reach Nairobi before schools closed for the weekend, but they were impatient to get there nevertheless.

So this was Africa. It wasn't as they had expected it to be. Yes, it was different, but it didn't feel <u>sufficiently</u> different. There were lots of birds around but no proper African animals, and it should have been much hotter. Clouds had drifted across the evening sun, and they hadn't expected clouds.

"Look over there! A buffalo!" shouted David suddenly. "Oh no, it's a cow."

They relaxed again.

"Is it racist to feel that Europeans are better than Africans as Customs officers?" asked Andrew.

"Probably," said Jim, "because you may not be allowing for the short time since Independence. It can't be easy taking on strange new responsibility."

"If Africans aren't good at the job, shouldn't you blame Europeans for not training them properly?" asked Richard.

"I think the snags are caused more by communication problems," said David. "I kept getting the feeling that they didn't understand why we were impatient, and that we didn't understand why they couldn't see what we thought was obvious."

They had been on the go for a couple of hours when they passed through a small settlement called Mackinnon Road. Shortly afterwards the tarmac ended, and the dirt surface gave a rougher ride. They slowed down to twenty miles an hour in case Charlie's tyres got sore. But twenty miles an hour soon became very tedious after the forty they had got used to, so they went at thirty as a fair compromise.

The evening was advancing, but no one liked to suggest they

stopped to camp just here, in the middle of nowhere. They were used to deserts, not African Bush. On Mokoto they had happily laughed about snakes and lions as a theoretical problem for the future, but now the future had come. Nobody actually said they didn't want to stop just yet, but all were hoping that they might come across something a bit more friendly than thorn scrub for their first night in Africa. It was not, of course, that they were nervous, but it would just be nice to have a little local advice about the procedures adopted in this area for...... well, lions and snakes for example. There would obviously be no problem really when you were used to things. So they were secretly relieved when Jim said, quite nonchalantly, that there seemed to be a farm or something over on the left, and how about having a look since it was getting late.

The farm or something looked a bit derelict as they got closer, and they wondered if it was deserted. But then a white man with a beard appeared. He was about their age, had a Scottish accent, and seemed friendly.

"Aye, make yourselves at home," said he. "This place used to be a motel, but the owner died. I use it as a base when I'm in the area." He waved them towards a row of wooden slatted doors off the stone verandah, and drove off to Mackinnon Road to get some petrol for his pick-up truck. The four intrepid explorers set up their camp beds and mosquito nets in one of the rooms. Then they sat on the verandah, and looked out over the belt of flat grassland in front of them. It looked a bit like a moat keeping the distant thorn scrub at bay. They were munching Mokoto bread and ham when the Scotsman returned.

"Can you move your Land Rover round to the side?" he asked. "I need a clear range to shoot over if the lions come back tonight. No, nothing to worry about," he added, probably noticing their expressions, "they're only after cattle. I'm a government Agricultural Officer, by the way. The name's Don." Don joined them for supper.

"Oh, I'm glad you chose that room," he said through a mouthful of Mokoto ham. "I've got a puff-adder in the one next door. Caught it yesterday. Didn't think to tell you 'til I'd gone. But it'll be pretty sleepy now, so probably wouldn't have bothered you anyhow. Biggest one I've seen. Want a look?" There was a choking noise. Andrew seemed to be having trouble with his coffee. Jim and David looked at each other. Was this fellow real? They hadn't been twelve hours in Africa and were already surrounded by lions and snakes. Maybe Don just had a sense of humour and was testing their naivetè.

"We'd love to see it!" said Jim.

"It's getting a bit dark now," said Don. Aha, thought David, we've called his bluff. But Don was back from his truck with a big torch and disappeared into the next room. The others peered cautiously through the window, and there in the torch beam, coiled up in a corner, was the biggest snake - well, the only snake - they had ever seen. Don poked it with a stick. The snake didn't respond. Don picked it up by the tail, and for a dreadful moment they thought he was going to hand it to them.

"Aren't they dangerous?" "Would you like some more coffee?" Richard and Andrew asked simultaneously through the window.

"Aye," replied Don. He returned the puff-adder to its corner, and rejoined them outside on the 'stoep', as he called the verandah. He loaded a rifle, and, while four pairs of newly-arrived eyes strained for lions in the dusk, gave them a summary of what they needed to know in Kenya. Camping was evidently quite safe if you stayed in a tent, but sleeping in the open wasn't recommended - hyenas being the main danger; their powerful jaws could remove a man's head with one bite. Lions rarely attacked humans, being more interested in cattle. The local farmers had lost many animals recently, which was why Don had been sent to the area.

They asked him if Kenya had changed since Independence. Was it still safe to travel? He laughed. Of course it was - unless you were in the far North of the country where bands of marauding Somalis were having a slaughter. That was probably why the Expedition hadn't been allowed through from Ethiopia. No, most of the country was entirely safe. The Mau Mau emergency had finished years before. Anyhow, Kenyatta had most of the Mau Mau generals - his old allies - in prison for robbery or murder or rape or something. No, the country would remain peaceful as long as Kenyatta was in charge. There was some discontent about rising unemployment, true, and taxes were higher than under the British, and the newspaper's parliamentary page was read for the laughs, and the civil service was getting pretty inefficient - but there would be no serious social unrest in Kenya, unlike the future for South Africa, in his opinion. Now, there mayhem was just waiting to happen, said Don, shaking his head. He knew of camps in several African countries which were training soldiers for the invasion.

It was very dark when they retired to their sleeping bags. The lions failed to make an appearance, but throughout the night the Cambridge to Capetown Expedition awoke at every sound - or, rather, three quarters of the expedition did, for nothing kept Richard from his sleep!

The rocky ridge looked out over thorn scrub to the horizon. Weird little hills rose here and there, incongruous gate-crashers looking embarrassingly conspicuous in the flat landscape. Overhead, the sky was heavy with clouds. There had been two or three showers already this morning - Don said it was very unusual for the time of year. Trust them to bring the British weather, thought Andrew! A tribe of baboons raced away over the rocks as he and David breasted the rise. Down below, they could hear the murmur of voices round the Land Rover, where Richard and Jim were helping Don to tie a dead buck onto the roof. Blood dripped down Charlie's side-panel.

When Don had suggested they came with him to replenish his workers' meat supply, they had jumped at the chance. A Safari had not featured at all in their plans, yet here they were, less than twenty-four hours on African soil, and already into the Boys' Own adventure stuff! Charlie had seemed quite at home bumping over the dirt tracks, weaving through the thorn trees like a veteran, or careering across the recently-burnt open areas. Don told them, in between calling directions to Richard at the wheel, that a syndicate of farmers ran five thousand cattle on a hundred thousand acres here. That was twenty acres to a cow - shared with wild animals, of course, and with an awful lot of thorn trees. They had found a herd of gazelle and Charlie had chased them for miles before Don could get a clear shot. Exciting stuff, and David had done the Shakespeare line about "gentlemen in England, now abed, shall think themselves accursed they were not here". But now, looking down at the smelly dead animal that had been something bounding and beautiful, they felt a bit ashamed of their enthusiasm for the contest - the poor buck had stood little chance against a powerful rifle. Still, as Andrew said, people had to eat something........

"Look!" called David, "A field gun!" There in a rocky hollow was the rusted one-wheeled remains of a piece of artillery. "It must be from the First World War!"

"Didn't your father fight here?" asked Andrew.

"Yes, he was in the East African Campaign, but a bit further South of here. These gun positions must have been used in the first phase, when the Germans were making incursions into Kenya from Tanganyika. Dad arrived a year or so later from South Africa with the King's African Rifles, in time for the second phase, which pushed the Germans out of Tanganyika."

"Was there a third phase?"

"Yes, Von Lettow Vorbeck, the German Commander, then spent the rest of the war fighting a guerrilla campaign around the whole area, being hounded but never brought to a decisive battle, and tying down huge numbers of allied troops - which was his original aim, to keep them from the European front."

"Sounds quite a hero," said Andrew as they picked their way back down over the wet rocks.

"He certainly ran rings round the English generals! It was only when Smuts, who had been a Boer guerrilla leader, took over command of the allies that they made any progress."

The others had finished loading their kill and were looking at a large pile of dung nearby. Don stuck his finger into it, and looked thoughtful. "It's barely warm," he grunted, "so they were here early this morning."

"What were?" asked David. Don sighed scornfully.

"Elephant," he said. "They come over from the Tsavo National Park and drink from the little dams I've made for the cattle. Since an elephant drinks fifty gallons a day, a herd of a hundred or more uses up all my water. We throw thunder-flashes at them to scare them off, but usually we have to shoot a couple before they'll go." The Expedition nodded understandingly.

Back at the old motel they unloaded Don's gazelle and thanked him for a memorable morning, then rejoined the main Nairobi road. The bush on either side was quite dense, but they did see a couple of dappled giraffe cantering away in slow-motion, and thought they saw some sort of fox. At Voi, they stopped an hour for a late lunch - and to their horror realised that the Mokoto ham had been left behind at the motel. For some reason this affected them more deeply than one would have expected, maybe because it was very good ham which would have lasted another two days, or maybe because it was their link with Mokoto. Gloomily, they ate a couple of biscuits with inferior meat paste.

Voi wasn't a very big place, but had a prominent First World War Memorial. They wandered over and read the inscriptions featuring the Royal North Lancs, the South African Mounted Infantry and the Rhodesian Horse. Andrew wondered aloud if the casualty rate had been high in a guerilla campaign.

"Dad always said that malaria and dysentery killed many more men than the Germans did," said David, "but even so it was a healthier place than the trenches of France."

A few miles west of Voi they were thrilled to see a trio of elephants feeding a hundred yards from the road. Andrew reached for his camera and got out of the cab. The largest elephant stopped feeding and sampled the wind, then, flapping his huge ears, he raised his tusks in their direction. Andrew quickly rejoined the Land Rover and they took off in some haste - not wanting, as they said, to disturb the wild life.

It was ten that evening before they stopped by the roadside somewhere near Emali. Andrew said he didn't mind sleeping on Charlie's roof for a change, Jim settled down on the stores in the back, and David's sleeping bag was on the front seats. These three felt themselves relatively secure from hyenas, but felt a bit anxious about Richard, underneath the Land Rover. However, in a couple of minutes his banshee snores put their minds at rest - surely nothing would risk approaching too close now! The other three lay awake and listened to him, and to the distant alarm calls of plovers, the occasional howl of a dog, and the much closer hum of mosquitoes. They were surprised how cold the night seemed, and tried to sleep.

"What does 'Uhuru Avenue' mean?" asked Richard, reading a street sign.

"I think it's 'freedom' in Swahili," replied Andrew, consulting his tourist guide. "This was probably 'Victoria Avenue' or 'King George Boulevard' before Independence." Nairobi impressed them immensely. This, surely, was superior to anything they had seen in Europe they thought, driving down the broad dual-carriageway. Not that the architecture was so grand, but the buildings were pleasantly spaced among trees and flowering shrubs, softening the impact of a large town.

They had started early, Richard chattering brightly at the wheel, to the accompaniment of bleary-eyed yawns from the others. Charlie had climbed gradually up to the "highlands" with frequent sightings of ostrich, giraffe and eland in the more open country. Their speed increased on the last forty miles, for the surface was tarmac again, and they arrived at Barclay's Bank shortly after opening time. At Nairobi's five thousand feet the morning air was cool in spite of the sunshine. They collected a joyful pile of mail, at which they had time only to glance before driving to the Ministry of Education. Fortunately it was open on Saturday mornings.

Afterwards, David wondered why he was surprised to find that all the staff at the front reception area were African. It was their country, after all, and they were now in charge. But for some reason he was a bit taken aback, and found himself speaking rather slowly and loudly, as if he expected communication to be difficult. He produced his "to whom it may concern" letter of introduction from UNESCO, which caused considerable excitement - and confusion, for no one could decide who should deal with it. David explained that it was really only a courtesy call, since offence might be caused if they visited schools without formal permission. At this, the desk staff brightened up and told him that the schools had just closed for the holidays.

There was a moment of horror. All four of them looked aghast at each other - they knew they had been delayed, but had not thought that term might be over! Then they realised that it didn't really matter, provided that they could find teachers to talk with, for the questions in their survey would have to be answered by the staff rather than pupils.

"May we have the addresses of your Secondary Schools?" asked David, loudly and slowly.

"They are all closed," came the reply.

"Yes, but we need to speak to some of the teachers." There was hurried consultation behind the desk, then a period when nothing seemed to be happening, when eye contact was avoided or met with anxious frowns. A higher official appeared, read the UNESCO letter and spoke to the lower officials in a rapid whisper - in which the phrase "experts from Britain" was heard. The higher official then escorted the "experts" upstairs, into a large office with a very large and entirely clear desk at which was seated an African in a tweed suit - no doubt a yet higher official. Hands were shaken and smiles exchanged, and a period of awkward silence ensued. Eventually, from an inner door a small Englishman appeared, who introduced himself as a Deputy Secretary. He was efficiency personified, and furnished them with lists of various schools, with their addresses and details of their staff.

"We're still a bit disorganised here," he smiled. "Change-over of personnel has been going on for only a few months, but I'm one of the last of the old guard! Now, anything else I can do to help? Let me 'phone a couple of the bigger schools which will have people about this morning, and fix up some appointments."

When they rejoined Charlie they had a programme of visits for Monday, Tuesday and Wednesday. At last the Project was about to start, and a mood of quiet elation filled the Land Rover. It remained only to find something to do until Monday. Lake Naivasha seemed a good idea - it was given a good write-up in the guide-book.

The road towards the Uganda border crossed the Rift Valley. Having been to the Dead Sea and the Red Sea, it was rather nice to catch up with this huge geological fault in a new continent. Lake Naivasha didn't impress the Expedition so much, but that may have been because they didn't get very close - the side road they took ended in a disused YMCA camp in a clearing, where they stopped for the night.

"Get away, you fools!" Jim shouted at a cloud of mosquitoes that greeted their arrival. "Don't you know I'm covered with insect repellent?" The mosquitoes took no notice, and supper was punctuated by regular slapping noises. A large mangy hound materialised from somewhere and sat hopefully nearby. David, whose turn it was to cook, offered their guest some rehydrated pea soup, which was cautiously sniffed and then declined.

"Tinned plums to celebrate Richard's Dip. Ed.!" David announced. The exam result had been one piece of news in the mail. Another letter forwarded from home had been from the British Council in Accra, saying they were arranging accommodation and visits for David when he reached Ghana "in October".

"You'll have to fly from South Africa to get there in time!" said Andrew. "Maybe you could collect Charlie later when it arrives by boat?" He lashed out at the swarm of insects trying to enter his mouth with a spoonful of plums and condensed milk. "Mosquito nets tonight!"

"You know that line 'the murmur of innumerable bees among the elms' that they used to give at school as an example of onomatopoeia?" asked David.

"Yes. What of it?"

"Bees aren't interested in elms. Sycamores, yes. Limes, yes. Elms - definitely not. But a poet could hardly write 'the murmur of innumerable bees among the sycamores'. Interesting that, isn't it?"

"David?"

"OK, I've shut up!"

It was cold in the middle of the Kenyan night. Under the netting, Jim buttoned up his coat and pulled up the rug. He put away the letters from Sal and switched off his torch. It was very quiet except for the breathing of the other netted shapes in their cocoons around the Land Rover. Why couldn't he sleep with their careless abandon? There was the faintest glow in the Eastern sky, against which he could just make out the outline of the hills around the lake........ And there was something else. Or was it his imagination? Was there something much nearer than the hills, something quite large, moving slowly........Yes! He could see it now very dimly, about a hundred yards away, but had it stopped? He thought so. No, whatever it was moved slightly. It was very big. About the size of ....an elephant? An ELEPHANT! Silently he rolled out from under the mosquito netting and crawled over to the next body, shook it gently and whispered "Keep very quiet!". Andrew was about to grumble that he had been very quiet before being wakened, but Jim's note of urgency stifled the impulse. In a few seconds all four of them were crouching in the gloom straining their eyes where Jim was pointing.

It couldn't have heard them. It hadn't moved closer. You could just see its ears flapping a bit against the slightly less black sky. Richard stretched his left leg. "Keep still!" hissed Jim. It was cold. How long would they have to stay like this before the elephant moved away? David was thinking how fortunate it was that Jim had been awake, else they might all have been trampled in their sleep. It was very cold. Why didn't the great creature go away?

"If we all shout suddenly and loudly it might run off," whispered Andrew.

"It might not," whispered David, who believed in examining both sides of an argument. "It might charge!"

"Shhhh!"

"Shhhh yourself!"

Time went by. It must be nearly dawn. You could just start to make things out. Jim looked around. Alongside, Andrew and David sat shivering. Richard seemed to have gone to sleep again in a crouching position. The elephant remained on the edge of the clearing, a huge shape looming tall and threatening. It was very big - the size of a tree, really. And it looked a bit like a tree now as the light swelled above the hills. In fact.................the branches moving gently in the breeze really did look awfully like ears flapping.

"Time for breakfast," announced Jim grimly.

It was a good day. The area was used for raising cattle, but again shared with game. The Expedition walked the green hills round the lake, and saw their first zebras. Shorts and vests had been abandoned for jeans and coats in the battle against insects, but the insects still seemed to be winning. A good deal of scratching took place.

That evening, since it was Sunday, and since it was their first Sunday in Africa, and since the project proper began on Monday, and since it seemed the right thing to do, Andrew and Jim led a short service by the rough wooden cross in the YMCA clearing. Then the congregation adjourned for a game of poker.

The deputy-head of Pumwani Secondary School, an expatriate

Englishman like most of the staff in secondary education, refilled the coffee cups - real Kenyan coffee. As if letting them use the school library as a base wasn't enough, he had insisted they came to dinner, and a splendid meal it had been. One of the guests was the Principal of the Teacher Training College, who was able to give the Expedition masses of useful background information.

"Don't for a moment suppose that the teaching here is inferior to that in Britain," he told them earnestly. "And university courses in East Africa are of a very high standard. The trouble is that the Africans have an ingrained conviction that everything foreign is better. The best students jostle to apply for second-rate American universities, whose ordinary degrees they rate more highly than a First at Makerere."

"But only a handful get to university level, Fred," said their host, "or to your teacher training college. I know the number of secondary school students has doubled since 1960, but I still don't have enough classrooms or teachers to take more than half the children who want to come. I'm not sure about the self-teaching 'Programmed Instruction' method these lads from Cambridge are looking at, but we need something to fill the teaching need!"

There were several other guests, including two African journalists from Botswana and Northern Rhodesia, who surprised the Expedition by saying that they thought the South African press as free as any in Africa.

"But doesn't the Apartheid government restrict reporting?" asked Andrew.

"The Afrikaaners are so thick they don't realise an article is attacking them until long afterwards!" laughed the Africans.

"Are you free to criticise the Kenya Government now?" asked Richard.

"There is no press censorship, but we can always be deported if we offend the regime! Besides, if you attack a speech by Kenyatta," the journalists shrugged, "he just denies saying it, or claims it was incorrectly translated from the Swahili. At least you got an honest response from the British." It seemed from this and other things said that the British were much more appreciated now that they were no longer in power! Nobody, however, seemed to have a good word to say for the Asians, who occupied the lower middle-class niche in Kenyan society.

"I've never met one who doesn't want to get something from you!" said someone from the end of the room. " But I suppose they are good businessmen."

"You can say that again!" said David. "I went to an Indian shop for a pair of sandals this afternoon - there were none my size, but the shop assistant was wearing a pair, and the proprietor made him take them off to see if they would fit me!"

Wednesday. The third day of school visits. Andrew was talking with an African secondary school headmaster. In theory all schools were now multiracial, but in practice they continued to serve their surrounding suburb, which would be ethnically homogeneous. On the wall of the classroom was painted "Treat the earth well - it was not given to us by our parents, but lent to us by our children." Andrew smiled approvingly, then looked out of the window over the surrounding countryside - not a tree to be seen for miles, all cut down for firewood. Andrew collected his notes. The headmaster had been very helpful, as had teachers at the other two schools he'd visited that day. The technique of "We need your help" instead of "We are here to help you" seemed to be working well, and teachers seemed enthusiastic about the potential for the new teaching method.

That evening they sat round the Pumwani library table in the light of the petrol lamp and prodded their rehydrated chow mein wearily. This survey stuff was hard work! But they felt they were starting to justify the expedition, and that was satisfying. David looked proudly at the piles of completed questionnaires - to think that they had doubted getting here at one stage! That afternoon he had gone back to see the Deputy Secretary at the Ministry of Education, to tell him that the teachers they had met were keen to try out Programmed Instruction. He had suggested that UNESCO might be approached to organise training workshops in Nairobi, like they had done in the Middle East and Nigeria. "If a formal request came from the Ministry here I'm sure they would be delighted to help." The Deputy Secretary had smiled sadly and said that it was up to the Minister, in the tone of voice which meant 'forget it'.

"They make big sacrifices here to go to school," said Jim. "Fees for a secondary school are between ten and twenty pounds a year, a fortune when the average African income is only twenty-five pounds a year!"

"Yes," said Andrew, "and do you know that one of the biggest problems they have with students here is hunger? A teacher told me that most children have one meal a day - in the evening when they get home - and during the day they find it hard to concentrate on maths when they are thinking of food! Maybe we should recommend eating as a better teaching aid than Programmed Instruction." He scratched his mosquito bites thoughtfully.

Chapter Nine - Tanganyika

The dehydrated meat bars had been kept for a special occasion, and the first night in Tanganyika seemed sufficiently special. Besides, Richard would be leaving when they got to Northern Rhodesia in a week's time, and if they waited much longer, he pointed out, it would seem that they were celebrating his departure. The evening sun flooded the summit of Mount Meru above the Training College in whose grounds they were camping. They had covered about two hundred miles that day over rough gravel roads. The open plains around Nairobi had been replaced by thickening bush as they climbed through the Masai country, passing groups of the tall red-cloaked tribesmen herding cattle. Andrew had informed them that the Masai greeting was "Sebi" to which the reply was "Ebi", but there had been no opportunity to test this in practice.

While Richard exercised his culinary skills on the meat bars, David crawled under the Land Rover to change the oil. From odd remarks percolating from beneath Charlie, it appeared that the nether regions were both prickly and bug-ridden. But at least the oil-release nut unscrewed very easily - this the onlookers deduced from the strong spluttering language that followed. Andrew, making suitably sympathetic noises, passed in a new oil filter - which would not fit, so the old one was refitted, but now leaked for some reason.

"How does Rover expect people to service their wretched machines if the approved spares with the prescribed code numbers won't fit?" snarled the oil-ridden servicer, emerging with attendant ants.

"Hush!" remonstrated Jim, "you'll hurt Charlie's feelings!"

"Have courage," soothed Andrew, doing his vicar's voice, "a dish of Richard's meat-bars will return joy to our cheeks."

"Actually," said Richard hesitantly, "I'm not so sure. Is it supposed to smell like this?" They unanimously agreed that it wasn't - what it did remind them of required description in terms of various bodily functions. The addition of large quantities of curry powder only partially masked the flavour, but a long-anticipated delicacy was not to be wasted, and it was consumed with brave smiles. Within an hour the spade was in constant use.

"Do you remember when we worried that the Expedition was too soft?" sighed Richard.

Next day, in Arusha, a suitable oil filter was found. Unfortunately, while it was being fitted at a local garage, there was a power cut, and the Land Rover was marooned on the top of a ramp-lift. They used the time to check that all the Nairobi mail had been dealt with. One letter was from the Senior Lecturer at Sheffield Psychology Department, requesting their assistance in determining the decision radius of lions. David explained that, as you approach an animal, there's a critical distance at which it has to decide whether to attack or retreat. Their task would be to measure this distance each time they came across a lion, to see if it was reasonably constant. Andrew wasn't sure whether the Senior Lecturer disliked David or had a sense of humour. "Or both," said David. Richard had by now found a handle to lower the ramp by hand - just as the power came back on.

"If we're to reach Tanga tomorrow," said Jim "we're behind schedule. Let's have lunch on the move." Now that they had eaten their way through half Charlie's load, there was more room in the back to spread meat-paste on biscuits and hand them through to the front cab.

The previous evening's sunshine had been a flash in the pan, and an East wind was now driving low drizzly clouds over the surrounding coffee plantations. Somewhere in the mist twenty miles to their left was Mount Kilimanjaro. Richard enquired why the guide books had not warned them that pullovers and mackintoshes were required gear for Tanganyika.

Shortly after passing through Moshi they turned off the tarmac towards Korogwe, and lurched, rattled and bounced their way over the worst roads they had yet encountered. At least the rain had stopped, but the mountains were still enveloped in mist.

"Did your father come this way?" Andrew asked David.

"He must have been in the area. Von Lettow Vorbek - I love saying that - was retreating down the Tanga railway, destroying it behind him as he went; and the Fifth South African Infantry were trying to outflank him - but never quite succeeding. They were always being delayed by ambushes." The Land Rover came to a stop. Ahead was a pole across the road and a group of Africans in khaki, pointing rifles at them.

A large man, wearing sergeant's stripes, motioned them to get out. They did. "What's the trouble?" asked Jim. The large sergeant looked very unhappy and frowned, as though trying to remember his lines.

"This is a police checkpoint. Have you any weapons?"

"No," said Jim.

"We do have a crowbar," said Andrew helpfully.

"What is a crowbar?" asked a smaller khaki man with a size fourteen neck in a size sixteen collar. The sergeant scowled at him and waved him to silence. "Do you have any ammunition for it?" Richard produced the crowbar - rifles were swung round to cover him. The sergeant sighed, as though he felt responsibility weighing heavily upon him. "Your passports?" he asked. These were produced from under the middle seat, and the police checkpoint gathered round to examine them.

"Whose is this?" asked the sergeant, holding David's passport open.

"Mine," said David. The sergeant frowned.

"It does not look like you."

"Ah, I've got a beard now." The size fourteen man looked round the sergeant's elbow. "And there he is smiling!" he pointed out. The sergeant nodded. "Laugh at me please," he commanded. David smiled nervously, but apparently it was sufficient to resemble the passport photo.

"Who is Thompson?"

"I am," said Jim.

"Father's name?"

"Also Thompson," said Jim.

"Also Thompson?" Eyebrows were raised and there was whispered comment at the coincidence, then general amusement. The tension evaporated in a chorus of laughter, and Charlie was waved on towards Tanga.

They motored some hours into the night, then camped by a sisal plantation. Too tired to bother with mosquito nets, they were awoken by a heavy rain shower, to find that any limb protruding from a sleeping bag had been extensively bitten, and itched horribly. Worse still, Jim had ear-ache. It was nearly dawn, so they had a muddy breakfast and pressed on, the sleeping bags tied on the roof to dry. Spirits were not high.

Having finished a large Secondary School and small Catholic Primary in Tanga, they returned to Korogwe, where they were to visit a Teacher Training Centre run by an Anglican Mission. The welcome there and the supper at the Principal's house erased their tiredness. They felt a little guilty accepting hospitality from a less than affluent institution, but salved their consciences by contributing tinned plums to the meal. It also helped to see the obvious pleasure taken by the staff in rare visitors from "home". The highlight for the Expedition was bread and butter! It was funny what you missed most.

Andrew enquired about wild animals in the area, and why they saw so few. He was told that there were still a few leopards around, but no lions had been seen recently. "Twenty years ago there were quite a lot," said one of the staff, "but as more land was cleared and the numbers of bush-pigs decreased, the lions would attack cattle. Then either they were shot or they moved to less developed country. I haven't seen one for three years." The Expedition was secretly relieved - you couldn't be too careful about a decision radius.

The next day was Sunday, and the College Chaplain, who came from Cumberland, conducted the 7 a.m. service entirely in Swahili. Richard wasn't sure that the incense and bells of Anglo-Catholicism were quite the thing for rural Africa, but he was captivated by the strikingly modern chapel. It was hexagonal in shape with white honeycomb walls open to the wind. He sat next to a lady who had been on the staff for fifty years, who had been interned by the Germans in 1914 and *walked* the seven hundred miles to the prison camp at Tabora! Now, that was an expedition of which to be proud, he thought.

The Fifth South African Regiment had been marching for months - it seemed like years. They had marched through heat and rain, succumbing in growing numbers to dysentery and fever, marching along the slopes of Kilimanjaro and now among the swamps of the Pangani valley, always just failing to trap the wily

Germans. There were plenty of skirmishes with a rearguard, but never a proper pitched battle. For the past week they had marched in the stench of decaying corpses of mules and horses, struck down by tsetse fly just as the troops were by mosquitoes. Forced march had followed forced march, and still they had not pinned down Von Lettow Vorbek's men. The transport wagons had been left far behind, and food was short, but the South African Irish Company - a rough lot, recruited from the same mining area - was happy: Last night Johnny McMullen had got a smelly piece of oxtail - better not ask from where - and they had feasted on oxtail soup, the first decent meal for days.

It was nearly dawn. There was stretching and yawning and swearing as disintegrating boots were tied up and jigger-flea eggs were dug out of feet with pen-knives. One of the Flying Corps aeroplanes had reported enemy troops near the village of Kangata yesterday - perhaps they didn't know the South Africans were so near. Another fast march might just catch them unawares. The order came for the Irish Company to lead off along the road South from Handeni.

"Call this a road?" muttered Pat Lawlor, as they pounded along the track of red earth.

"Easier than cutting your way through thorn bushes," replied George Moore alongside. "Look on both sides - you can't see more than ten yards through that scrub!"

"How the hell are we supposed to find the Germans in this lot?" Pat slapped at the insects on his neck.

"We'll find them easy enough when they fire," said Bartholomew from behind them, "and I reckon that's what we're supposed to be - targets. Then everyone else will know where they are. Still, another bloody section will be scouting this afternoon."

But the afternoon didn't come for Bartholomew. It was about nine o'clock when the German machine guns opened up from close range. Half the Irish Company were hit in the first burst. The other half dived for the thorns and fired back, lying as close to the red earth as they could get, for the bullets were coming at ground level.

After a long time the shouting and firing and swearing and crying stopped. Nothing moved in the thornscrub.

"I'm hit, George," said Pat - quite quietly, as if he didn't want to be overheard.

"So am I. I can't feel my legs."

"You're good at praying," gritted Pat, "say one for me. ....
And, George?"

"What?"

"When you get back to Jo'burg will you do something for me?"

"Don't talk nonsense, man. Do it yourself......... They'll have us
back at the Handeni dressing station in no time."

"The old woman in the shop by the mine gates. I owe her half a
crown. Will you pay her for me?"

The Expedition stopped at a Military Cemetery at a place called
Handeni, but found no names that David could remember his father
mentioning. So they drove along the undulating earth road to a place
called Kangata, a small village of damp thatched huts that looked like
fungi past their best. The schoolmaster in the little thatched
schoolroom spoke English, and translated for his father, who didn't.

"Yes, I was a small boy then. I remember the soldiers coming
and the fighting. It began early in the morning and went on all day.
There are graves down the hill there, if you would like to see." About
a mile from the road, in a clearing in the trees, was a rectangle of clean
gravel inside green-painted railings, with a row of neat white
headstones. And there they were - Pat Lawlor, Johnny McMullen,
Bartholomew Fitzmaurice, and half a dozen others, each with 20th.
June 1916 after their names.

It was warm and quiet in the little glade. David's father had
always wanted to find the place his friends had been buried, and now
his son had done it for him. David found himself remembering lines
from The Listeners by Walter de la Mare:

"Tell them I came, and no one answered,
That I kept my word,' he said.................."

What came next? There was something about "Never the least stir
made the listeners......." He felt his eyes misting up, and followed the
others back to the village. In the green railings, thousands of miles
from Ireland, or Johannesburg, or anywhere, the headstones were
warm in the sunshine, and "silence surged softly backward......"

The schoolmaster showed them his schoolroom, with the thatch
propped up at the edges to make a porch. They asked him what

would help education in the village. "Paper and pencils," he said earnestly.

"Little scope for computers," sighed Richard as they drove away.

"We are not enjoying ourselves, honest!" murmured David, lying on the warm sand near the channel into Dar Es Salaam harbour.

"We are working terribly hard," agreed Richard, eating an orange. Actually it had been a very busy day. A visit to the Ministry of Education, where most of the officials were "just out at the moment", had been made worthwhile by the very helpful "ex-pat" chief inspector. The chief aim was greater literacy, he told them; presently only fifty per cent of six-to-eleven-year-olds were in school, and often a teacher was spread between two or three classes, teaching one while the others did set work. Half the primary schools were operated by Christian missions, without which the task would have been overwhelming. Tanganyika was lucky to have a common national language, Swahili, in which primary school children were taught; but secondary education was carried out in English, there being few text books written in Swahili; and being taught in your second language was a handicap.

They had persuaded Jim to go to the hospital in Dar-Es-Salaam to have his ear treated, and had gone with him to make sure. The doctor had diagnosed an infection "caused by something in the water" and prescribed accordingly. Then they had pitched their tents on the beach and had swam in the warm evening sea - except for Jim, who wasn't allowed to get his ear wet.

Camping next to them was a party of German students in a Volkswagen. Andrew wondered whether to ask them if they knew anything about Von Lettow Vorbeck, but thought it might not be tactful. The Germans warned them about thieves, having had a leather jacket removed from inside their car the previous night. The Expedition sympathised knowingly, and locked anything worth stealing inside Charlie.

A glorious sunrise between crimson clouds awoke them. Blue, blue water lapped against white powdery sand beneath the palm trees. A fleet of little sailing boats glided out for their day's fishing on the Indian ocean. "I could get to like this life," announced Andrew, returning from his swim. "Where are we going this morning?" He and Richard went to glean information from the Civil Service Training Centre, dropping David at the British Council Office, while Jim, whose ear was still painful, stayed on the beach to do the washing - and commiserate with the Germans, who had been robbed again ("but we just put the camera down for a moment!").

The arms of the Expedition reassembled for lunch. Jim was found in deep conversation with a passing Catholic priest who was advocating the need for a greater stress on philosophy and literature in African education. He was also analysing the difference between a scientist and an educated scientist, and urging increased vigilance against communist infiltration. Jim's part in the conversation was a listening role.

"Would you like to join us for water-biscuits and tinned cheese?" asked Richard. The priest suddenly remembered something he had to do, and hurried off.

Over lunch David repeated the fascinating story that the British Council staff had told him. A sixteen-year-old lad on a year's VSO had arrived the previous September, expecting to help build a school in Burundi (wherever that was). Instead, when he got there, he found thousands of Watutsi refugees fleeing from persecution in the Congo. He organised them into parties to build shelters. Then, realising that this was no short-term problem, he urged them to plant crops and build mud-huts, tasks for which they showed no enthusiasm. So he announced that the temporary shanties would have to be dismantled by the end of the month. Little action took place, so at the end of the month he began burning down the make-shift hovels. In hindsight this was probably a risky strategy, and there was indeed fury and uproar, but they began building permanent huts! The lad had now nearly finished his year as Policeman, Administrator, Engineer and Midwife - he was certainly far more than a year older!

"Makes our project seem rather tame!" smiled Jim.

The Professor of Education at the University College, just outside the town, impressed them immensely. He had given up a better "career" job at London University for the challenge of starting this new department, and the Expedition felt that his warmth and enthusiasm would ensure success. His job was to produce enough secondary school teachers to cope with the increasing flow due to emerge from the primary school programme, although "it would be cheaper to send my undergraduates to overseas universities than start up this new faculty," he admitted with a grin. "But how do you put a price on self-sufficiency?"

Back at the beach, which seemed to operate as a sort of clearing house for travellers, their new neighbours were a couple from Nebraska who had travelled to Kenya by motorbike through North Africa, Sudan and Ethiopia.

"We were told it was too dangerous!" protested the Expedition.

"It was!" said the Americans. "Two people in the military convoy taking us through Northern Kenya were wounded by gunfire. But it will add colour to our lecture tour when we get back." It transpired that they were to lecture on African Education ("It's getting kinda popular") and they had come to a surprising conclusion - that Africa would be better with less education.

"Educate a girl in Sudan and she then costs four times as many cattle to marry! Besides, notice the kids in bare feet - they always smile and wave, while the ones with socks, obviously the educated ones, just scowl and look unhappy. No, Sir, education causes more problems than it solves: it breaks up the tribal system, arouses political ambition, contributes to greater longevity and therefore food shortage, and it fans discontent with things as they are - providing a fertile breeding ground for communism." The bikers were clearly very serious about their theory - funny people, Americans.

Jim was still having painful days and sleepless nights in spite of the antibiotic tablets. The other three, without wishing to show it, were getting worried. What did you do when the only hospital had done its stuff without much effect? Being ill while travelling is no fun. It was decided - by a three to one majority - that Jim would do absolutely nothing but rest for the next two days, avoiding swimming (or any other enjoyment), while the others finished off the school visits.

The Americans heard that the Expedition was leaving soon, and suggested it would be great to travel in convoy towards Northern Rhodesia - and, hey yes, the Land Rover would have room to carry some of their stuff. The Expedition shuffled its collective feet and declined, saying something weak about their schedule of frequent school stops not being fair on the Nebraska couple.

"It's hard enough putting up with people we like," said Andrew afterwards. "Actually, do you realise we've done nine weeks without falling out? Nothing but sweetness and light!"

"I think we may have criticised each others' driving on occasions," said Richard.

The friendly scent of woodsmoke in the darkness told them they must be approaching a village - a good place to stop for the night before they were too close. They had eaten a quick meal earlier that evening, and then jolted on over the rough and rutted road for an extra couple of hours, so that they could reach Mbeya next morning. It took only five minutes to pitch camp around Charlie, but there was the usual pre-sleep paperwork to do. "Budget's in the black," said Jim. "We didn't expect petrol to be only four shillings a gallon here." Doing the accounts helped take his mind off the earache.

The others, too, were bringing notes and diaries up to date by the light of the petrol lamp, which was much brighter since Andrew had fitted a new mantle. Andrew was good at stoves and lamps, just as Richard was with Land Rovers. Charlie had had its first mechanical problem that morning (the oil-seal didn't count because it hadn't been Charlie's fault). There had been a horrendous rattling noise from underneath, and Richard had disappeared in the direction of the trouble. He reported "a disconnected exhaust manifold", which sounded serious, if not terminal. The others were immensely impressed and relieved when five minutes later he reported "Fixed". They asked how he had managed such a feat. "Tightened the nut again," said Richard, which brought the awed respect to an abrupt end.

Places and names and people got a bit blurred after three days on the road. Morogoro was yesterday, a small town on a plain of sisal. At the Teacher Training College a chap from the Potteries (Burslem was it?) told them that he wished he could turn the clock back to when he arrived in 1930: "The locals were happy simple folk then. Now they've learned to want money and, when they get it, more money - and they're no longer happy."

Next had come the Great Ruaha River, and then Iringa in the hills, where the Asian school had been very unhappy about becoming racially mixed, fearing that standards would fall. Then back to the flatter scrubland, with giraffes browsing by the roadside - the first large animals they had seen for a fortnight. There were few other vehicles on the road, but many bicycles,and frequent walkers who would wave them down for a lift. Soft-hearted Richard would lean out of the window in passing, and explain that regretfully they were a bit short of space, but otherwise it would have been a pleasure.........

David had found gorgeous-looking bunches of bananas in a village market, and had bought some as a special treat - unfortunately the bananas turned out to be plantains, tasting more like raw parsnips. You got days like that.

"The foot you heal is the one that kicks you," said Andrew thoughtfully, packing up his diary and examining his sleeping-bag for snakes, just in case.

"What has that to do with anything?"

"Nothing really. It was just something one of the teachers said this afternoon."

"Oh."

"Good-night."

"Good-night."

September 5th. The border with Northern Rhodesia - or Zambia as it was to be called next month at Independence. There was a young white customs officer on duty who wanted them to fill in forms declaring "capital assets". They explained that they were just passing through, not settling in the country; but he got quite stroppy, so they gave in and listed the value of travellers' cheques, food reserves and Aunt Madge's jam spoon. Andrew muttered something about "blind bureaucracy" and David couldn't resist needling the official by saying, in a voice just loud enough to be overheard, that things might be better next month when the Africans took over.

Outside the Customs Office, a policeman urged them to take care on the road South. A nearby township had recently been attacked and two policemen killed by the Lushindi. "The what?" they enquired. Evidently the Lushindi were members of a fanatical religious sect led by an eccentric prophetess, called Alice, who were creating a serious nuisance, burning villages and shooting the occupants. The Lushindi smeared themselves with sacred grease which made them invulnerable to bullets - a conviction that was strangely resistant to the frequent deaths of their members from gunfire. The Expedition was enthralled, but not unduly alarmed, for it was clearly just some local African difficulty.

"Tell that to the reservists who have to mow them down with machine guns - women and children and all," sighed the policeman.

They stopped on the Saturday night near the small town of Isoka. If Richard caught the train at Kapiri Mposhi on Monday he could get to his school in time for the start of term. But Kapiri Mposhi was still four hundred miles of dirt road South. So they started very early on Sunday morning, and did a hundred and fifty miles before noon.

"We used to prattle away for the first hour, then gradually dry up," said Andrew. "This morning I don't think anyone has spoken at all."

"Sunk in gloom over Richard's impending departure," yawned David.

"Or," said Richard, "because there is not a lot to say about mile after mile of empty road and uninterrupted woodland."

"We'll miss you and your solid reliability," said Jim. "Fifty percent of the Expedition's common sense goes with you, not to mention your mechanical genius!"

"And you'll have to play three-handed bridge," laughed Richard. David was wondering suspiciously how the other fifty percent of the common sense was to be allocated.

The afternoon miles slipped behind them in a cloud of dust. The land was monotonously flat, the corrugated road was neither better nor worse than usual, and there were a lot of trees which all looked the same. It was very warm in the Land Rover, so, to keep the driver awake, someone suggested playing 'I Spy With My Little Eye', It didn't last long - D for dust and T for trees exhausted the menu. They relapsed into silence.

"I was thinking," said Jim, some time later, "that although you couldn't do something like this without a vehicle, it does insulate you from the places you go through. How many Africans have we met, really? A few teachers, yes, and talked about teaching. But what have we learned about the people themselves? The only conversation in any depth has been with other Europeans. In fact we avoid Africans by camping away from villages. I know that there are good reasons, but it does seem a pity! I suppose we'll have to leave it to Richard to get to know real Africans."

"What are we having for supper?" asked David. "How about tinned chicken for Richard's farewell banquet? Thank goodness there are no meat bars left!"

It was nearly dusk before they stopped at a clearing by the roadside. Three hundred and fifty two miles in eleven hours driving. Not bad, but hard on cramped limbs, so after supper they strolled a way along the road in the twilight. Their clearing turned out to be just round the corner from a larger clearing, where it seemed there had once been a village - there were remains of houses here and there. And then they noticed that some of the remains were smouldering. As one, they froze and listened. It was very quiet - creepy almost. Then they realised they hadn't seen anyone else for hours. It was a nervous Expedition that quickly returned to Charlie.

"The Lushindi?" whispered Andrew.

"If so, they've long gone," whispered Richard, wondering why they were whispering. Nobody slept much that night, and it was a relief to get away in the early morning sunshine and leave the still-smoking ruins behind.

The road was deserted, and they had the trees and the dust to themselves. About mid-morning, Charlie skidded in some loose gravel, went into a ditch, rolled across the road, and ended on its side in the ditch opposite.

Chapter Ten - Rhodesia

The long loud grinding noise finally stopped. A tangle of limbs inside the cab separated and two sets of arms and legs struggled through the door above. Jim remained where he was - his arm had been out of the window and Charlie had rolled on top of it. Another dazed body emerged unsteadily from the back door, and joined the two regarding the scene in stunned silence.

"I say, could anyone help here?" said Jim's voice inside. Realisation seeped into their fuddled minds. Trapped arm. Must raise the Land Rover. Crowbar in the back somewhere. All together now. With a heave Charlie tottered to its wheels in a shudder of dust. Jim gritted his teeth and slowly drew his arm back inside. They all rushed to help him out. "Are you OK?" What a stupid thing to say when he had just had a ton of Land Rover on his arm. What should they do? It was probably broken. Savlon wouldn't help much. Was there a hospital at Kapiri Mposhi? But that was twenty or thirty miles away. Charlie would need unbending before it would move.

OK... if they could just get the crowbar in like that.... yes, and then if the front wing was levered off the wheel ....

A car stopped alongside them. The driver introduced himself as the Anglican Diocesan Clerk, and could he help? He was on his way to Broken Hill, where there was a hospital. He'd take Jim and send back a tow-truck from Kapiri Mposhi. Richard said he'd go to look after Jim, and then they could all meet up later before Richard caught his train.

"Yes, there's a train from Kapiri Mposhi to Choma tonight," said the Diocesan Clerk. "Where are you heading? Mpanza! Not St. Mark's College by any chance? I'm on the Governors, and we were expecting a teacher from England!"

And off they went. Andrew and David sat in the sun and compared bruises. They had felt nothing at the time, and agreed that their main recollection was a puzzled feeling - what was all that noise and why were things going round?

"It could have been a lot worse!" sighed David.

"And then along comes the only car we have seen for ages! And lo and behold, it's Richard's Diocesan Clerk!"

"Incredibly fortunate!"

"Providential might be a better word."

"But poor Jim - he must have been in agony!"

An hour or so later two Africans arrived with a truck and attached a rope to Charlie. David said he'd steer, and urged them to drive carefully since he couldn't see much through the shattered windscreen. They set off with a violent jerk, and roared along the road at forty mph, throwing up clouds of dust and gravel. David, who hadn't driven at this speed even when Charlie was fit, shouted that he couldn't see where they were going - to no avail, the truck's engine drowned his voice. He couldn't remember feeling so helpless. Clenching the wheel desperately, he squinted into the clouds of dirt, alternately screaming "Slow down!" and snarling terrible things to himself about Africans. It was a merciful relief to come upon tarmac after a few miles - at last he could see where they were going. But the tow-truck now speeded up to fifty, with Charlie weaving precariously behind.

They finally reached Kapiri Mposhi, and the Africans, beaming happily, came round and untied the rope. David was sitting quite still. His lips were moving, as if he wanted to say something, but just couldn't find the words. After some time, breathing heavily, he dragged his hands away from the steering wheel. Meanwhile Andrew negotiated with the Yugoslavian garage proprietor for running repairs.

In mid-afternoon Richard and Jim rejoined them. Jim had a cracked bone in his wrist, and sported a gleaming white plaster cast. Meanwhile, the Yugoslav had reported that he had straightened out the left wing, and that the engine and transmission were undamaged ("In spite of the tow!" David muttered). It should get them to the Copperbelt next day, where they had friends whom they were due to visit - Noel, an engineer, and Viv, a doctor. Both would come in very useful!

The town of Kapiri Mposhi was not a major metropolis - it had eight Europeans, and the public lighting went off at 7.40 pm. The Expedition spent a subdued evening - no one could summon up much cheer. Everything had been going so well, and now - broken bone and crumpled Land Rover. How would they meet their schedule? And how would the Nigerian Mission Hospital like the state Charlie was in? Things were looking horribly gloomy.

Richard's train left at midnight from the station across the road. The residual team of three came back to the garage feeling tired, depressed and cold. They arranged themselves around the Land Rover in defensive mode, one by each of the doors that no longer closed properly, and tried to sleep. Looking back afterwards, they were not sure if that night they wished that they had never come, but they certainly got close to it.

They awoke at dawn, cold and miserable. Jim insisted on cooking porridge (one-handed). A crackly telephone line was found to give Noel and Viv in Kitwe notice of their proximity and condition, and Charlie set off to limp the hundred miles North-west. They drove in silence for most of the way, each buried in his own thoughts. Gradually the positives came to outweigh the negatives, and by the time Kitwe was reached, life was beginning to seem liveable again. It was further upgraded by their welcome. Noel organised remarkably effective and inexpensive repairs for Charlie, and Viv concentrated on repairing Jim. "The arm's not too bad," she said, "but I'll need to do some tests on your ear infection, which seems to have spread to the mastoid." David and Andrew nodded knowingly, wondering what a mastoid was. There followed four days of marvellous food and real beds. Battered morale was on the mend.

David had the address of a cousin on the Roan Antelope copper mine, so he went over to Luanshya to see him. The mine's training department was quite interested in Programmed Instruction - maybe they could use it for teaching Chikabanga, for instance. Chikabanga was the lingua franca of the copper belt. Since African trainees came from many different tribal groups with different languages, communication was by means of this sort of pidgin African. No matter what race or tribe you came from, you should know, for example, that "Bos op sterek kapata" meant "Be careful of the detonator". David particularly liked the word for absentee - "Lofa"!

He had thought that, when mining, you crouched in the dark and wet, and was surprised to find broad well-lit tunnels. The highlight of the day, he told the others, was meeting another

Manxman. Drilling at the workface two thousand feet down was "a Quayle from Douglas" he said in a voice of amazement. Andrew wanted to say "So?", but stopped himself in time, for it was clear that David's sense of humour didn't extend to frivolous remarks about his nation.

The police arrived one evening while they were at Noel's to enquire if the bearded newcomers had entered the country legally. Evidently they were suspected of being mercenaries from the Congo - a suggestion that gave the Expedition no little satisfaction. Katanga was just to the North of them, and the rebellion there was evidenced by fleeing missionaries - and a ready supply of UN Relief goods on the black market. Just along the road from Kitwe was the town of Ndola, where Dag Hammersjold, the UN Secretary General, had been killed in a plane crash a short while before.

Andrew and David sat in the hot sunshine, listening to the roar of the Victoria Falls. Charlie posed beside them, slightly dented at the corners but otherwise in fine fettle. Jim had been grounded at Kitwe; his ear was improving, but Viv had insisted he stayed until cultures could be grown to identify the infection type. So Andrew and David had driven South to do the education visits around Lusaka - not over-keenly let it be said, for rehydrated soup and damp sleeping-bags lacked the attraction of Kitwe hospitality.

The spray from the huge waterfall hung over the gorge below them, nourishing a permanent rainbow. They had heard so much about the Falls that they had not allowed themselves to expect too much, in case it would be like the pyramids - grand, but not living up to the reputation. The reality of the thundering spray and foaming cataracts left them searching for words - awe-inspiring came closest. They felt uncomfortably like tourists, but nothing much could be done in Lusaka until Monday, tomorrow. Last night they had visited Richard's school, off the Lusaka to Livingstone road, where he was beginning his three-year stint. Three years! They had masked their pity with a pretence of envy, but had later shaken their heads and agreed that three months in Africa would be enough for them. They were loath to criticise the hygiene at St. Marks College, but were today limiting their intake to kaolin powder and water biscuits.

"What were Viv's Nyasaland houseboys called?" mused Andrew. "Philemon.....?"

"Philemon, Gallop and Flywell," smiled David. "And weren't they great!"

"Worked like..." Andrew stopped himself, "...like Trojans. I wonder how much they were paid?"

"Why? Feeling guilty at oppressing the natives? I should think they earn a lot more than the average African. Mind you, not as much as the African mine workers - they get a wage that would be good in England, sometimes a thousand pounds a year. That's vicar level, isn't it?"

"It's the inequality that worries me," frowned Andrew. "Maybe African workers are quite happy with their wages, but it just hurts that if you have white skin you are paid a lot more for doing the same thing."

"You're getting as bad as Jim! The Copper Mine people were telling me that, with Independence coming up, they are being pressured to promote Africans into 'European' jobs at European pay."

"Good thing, too."

"But the trouble is that they can't do the job with anything like European efficiency. Yes, I know you're going to say they haven't had the educational background, and better training will solve the problem. Maybe you're right, but the people who've lived here for years say it is a cultural thing that will take generations to change. Where's the spade? I'll be back in a minute."

The road towards Lusaka had stretches of good tarmac and stretches of the tarmac double strips - the latter requiring vehicles to move their left-hand wheels onto the dust and gravel when they met. With practice it worked well, but it always seemed that Charlie was to leeward of the clouds of sand thrown up, and the taste of grit was constantly in the driver's mouth. They had become quite nonchalant about camping, since there seemed a marked lack of wild animals in Northern Rhodesia. That day, as dusk approached they were looking for a suitable stopping place when they saw something lying in the road ahead of them - it looked like a body. It was a body.

Having been warned about ambushes and robbery, they kept the engine running and carefully scanned the surrounding bush before getting out. There was a bicycle in the ditch nearby - evidently the chap had crashed, and the smell of alcohol suggested why (the locals drank seriously, using not pint mugs but gallon buckets). The body was alive and seemed to have injured a shoulder, but wasn't anxious to be helped, merely requesting to be left to die. Andrew and David thought it a better idea to haul him into the Land Rover like a sack of mealies, and at the next village to enquire if there was a doctor around. A collection of laughing youths told them there was a clinic, and escorted them there, where they left their charge with a white-coated attendant. It was only later they learned that he was the local witch-doctor! Not that there was anything wrong with his mixture of herbal medicine and faith-healing - and besides, there was no other type of doctor anywhere in the area.

The approach of Independence seemed to be causing no great excitement in Lusaka. The Expedition had found a measure of obstreperous national pride in the countries further North, but here there was only polite interest - maybe they had no great faith in the promises of their politicians. "Well," one white business man told them, "they are expecting better houses and more pay, and the trouble will start when they get tired waiting - so we had better get out before that happens!"

The Ministry of Education was not particularly helpful. Probably they were too occupied with the imminent reorganisation required by Independence to be bothered with students in Land Rovers. What became clear was that the education system suffered greater "wastage" than even Tanganyika's: over seventy thousand children started primary education each year, and about ten thousand completed the eight year course. And of these only a third would go on to secondary education. It didn't look as if the years of British administration had a great deal to boast about. True, an increasing number were getting some primary education, but what benefit was this when most would return to subsistence farming as the only occupation available? True, a handful had been sent to universities abroad, and from these would come the political leaders. However, in a population of cabinet ministers and agricultural labourers there were huge gaps to fill. How long would it be before the school system could produce managers and technicians, a middle class to staff industry, public services and administration - and in sufficient numbers?

Charlie's camp site for the Lusaka visit was a field next to the open-air cinema. With binoculars you could just about follow the action, but you had to imagine the dialogue. A phone call to Kitwe brought the good news that Jim was progressing well and would travel down to Lusaka with Noel the next day. Andrew and David were finding interviewing with two much harder work than they were used to, and the prospect of a fifty percent increase in the team cheered them considerably. When Jim arrived, they had finished gleaning information from the Ministry of Education, and had visited Prince Philip High School, Chalimbana Technical College and a couple of primary schools, but there still remained work for another couple of days.

One complication in producing educational materials for primary schools in Northern Rhodesia was the large number of mother-tongues found in the country - it was not economically practicable to publish school books in more than four of the commoner languages. Another problem which had not occurred to them was a social one: because families thought it more important to send sons than daughters to school, there was a serious shortage of educated wives for the intellectual elite!

A friend of Noel's from South Africa took them to lunch at the Ridgeway Hotel (as much as you could eat for seven shillings and sixpence). He told them that the weather further South, where they were headed, was most unusual. The Transvaal had had the first snow in living memory. Jim recalled that old George at Emmanuel always blamed the atomic bomb tests for ruining the weather.

"Good heavens," said Andrew, "it's mid September! We've only got a fortnight left!" They had bought a copy of an English newspaper in Lusaka, and were reading it over breakfast at Kariba, where they had camped the night. The world had been going on without them: Tokyo was having Olympic Games and Britain was going to have an election. It was strange to realise that no one else seemed particularly bothered about African Education. They looked out over the lake melting into the early morning haze. Here and there little islands dotted the vast expanse of water. Many of them would disappear in the next year or so as the water level rose, for round the corner at the entrance of the Kariba Gorge was the sweeping curve of the highest dam in the world. Forty miles off their direct route, it was well worth the detour. They had been amazed how anything built out of concrete could look so splendid.

Charlie drove across the road on top of the dam. There was still much work taking place on the hydroelectric systems, and it would be a long while before water torrented forth, but the huge grey concave wall was complete. Jim held David's feet while he hung over to photograph the toy bulldozers down below.

"In twelve days time I'll be back with Sal," murmured Jim dreamily. Andrew groaned - it looked like they were going to have a daily count-down.

"Just concentrate on the here and now, for Pete's sake," exclaimed David, who felt distinctly vulnerable suspended over the parapet. He didn't like heights at the best of times, and the ant-like figures below made him feel very uncomfortable.

"Who is this cousin of Sal's we're going to visit?" asked Andrew, when David had regained safety. "It seems a bit of a nerve to just land in on people we don't know!"

"Sal says they won't mind at all - in fact they're keen to meet us," Jim reassured them. "They farm near a place called Shibani - I think we have to go towards Bulawayo. It's quite a way, but since it's Friday, and since we can't do anything useful in Salisbury until Monday, it seems the logical thing to do, don't you think?" They did.

A day's journey took them through Sinoia and Gwelo. They slept in a lay-by and arrived at Hokonui Ranch in time for breakfast the next day. Garfield and Grace had come to Southern Rhodesia from New Zealand as missionaries, and had started a school at Dadaya. After some years Garfield had gone into politics, and had been Prime Minister from 1958 to 1960. But his liberal views caused dissent in his party, and he had handed over leadership. Now a new government was in power, headed by a man called Smith, who was resisting the trend to the majority rule seen further North. But Britain was applying pressure, and Prime Minister Smith had just returned from London where he had agreed to "consult African opinion".

"So he's going to talk to the tribal chiefs," smiled Garfield, "who depend on the government for their jobs! They will say what they are told to say, and that will delay progress a while, but majority rule will come eventually."

The house was situated on the crest of a ridge, three miles of very rough track away from the main road. On one side an escarpment dropped steeply to where a river nudged its way through the scrub. There had been a severe drought that year, and the landscape was brown and brittle. The Expedition sat on the terrace looking towards the strangely shaped Matopa Hills in the distance. Looking down to the river, you could make out the shapes of hippos under the surface, bouncing in slow motion along the bed of the deeper pools, raising puffs of mud like miniature shell bursts. A car was climbing slowly up from the main road, and as it got closer they could make out the police insignia on its side. Garfield explained that the police kept a close eye on him, regarding him as a dangerous African sympathiser. After all, he smiled, not only had he advocated votes for blacks, but he regularly visited African leaders in detention! One of these, Joshua Nkomo, had been a pupil at the local Dadaya School.

The African house staff had locked the cupboards before the car reached the front door - the white police had a poor reputation for honesty among the black population - and were looking out suspiciously as two young officers in khaki uniforms and brown jack-boots got out. Garfield went to meet them, but it was his daughter, Judith, whom they wanted to see. She had been involved in an anti-government demonstration in Salisbury, and was summoned to appear in court. Since she was still in Salisbury, the police were re-directed, and wound their bumpy way back down the drive.

Andrew asked Garfield how a missionary teacher came to be a cattle-rancher. "Because," he said, "in 1946 there was a great shortage of fencing wire! We saw a government notice in the paper advertising seventy miles of game fence 'in very poor condition' near here. Now, we knew the area, and that the fencing was in quite good condition, so we wondered if someone wanted it sold cheaply! Grace and I walked the area again, checked the fence, and put in a bid. It turned out to be the highest by a long way, but still enabled us to sell it off to local farmers for a profit with which we bought this ranch. Forty thousand acres sounds a lot, but it takes about fifteen acres to support one beast. Then we rented off thousand-acre strips, each with river frontage, to African farmers. Not that this made us many friends among the whites, who either thought us mad because it could never work, or dangerous, because it might!"

"And did it?" asked David.

"Yes. The cold-storage people provide cattle for fattening and pay for the weight increase when they take them back for slaughter. The Ndebele are very good at looking after animals. They need some help with things like book-keeping, but by and large they manage very well."

"That's tremendous!" said Jim.

"So, Mr. Psychologist," grinned Andrew, "why do you say that Africans have lower intelligence than Europeans?"

"Different, not lower!" riposted David hotly. "I never said they had lower intelligence. OK, the usual Intelligence Tests that we use in Britain show a difference of four or five years between African and European Intelligence."

"But they are designed for people in Britain," put in Jim.

"Absolutely, I was going to say that, if I had been allowed to finish. I was going to say that there is no intelligence test equally fair to both groups. Put an Oxford graduate in the Kalahari and ask him to find water, and he wouldn't do as well as an African. Give an African child a test which asks questions in English, a foreign language, about houses with rooms and toys with wheels, when he lives in a round hut and plays with sticks, and he is at a disadvantage. So, if you define intelligence as 'the ability to solve problems in a technological society' clearly a European will come out ahead, because he's had more experience of the background."

"How would you define intelligence?" asked Garfield.

"The ability to learn," said David. "that's the simple definition. And if you could design a test which didn't depend on society and culture -and I don't think you can - I would expect there to be little difference between the average African and the average European. After all, students at Dar es Salaam Technical College have a seventy or eighty percent pass rate in City and Guild exams in Motor

Mechanics and Electrical Installations, about the same as you'd find in England. So if the teaching is good, and there is enough time, there is no ceiling to African achievement. But give a simple maths problem to a child who has not come across the concept of number, and you might think he's stupid."

"Yes," said Grace, "the Africans round here can find our maths lessons very difficult. They are a cattle-owning race, and have twenty words or more for cows with different characteristics, a brown cow or a lame cow or one with a twisted horn, but no single word for cow. So how do they count their animals?"

"Could it be," suggested Jim, "that they notice when a particular animal, that they know as an individual, is missing? I've been told that there are tribes with two words for numbers - 'more than six' and 'less than six' - but I'm sure they know if they've lost one of their ten cattle."

"The Zulu word for eight," put in David, "means literally 'that being found with two hands less two fingers'. Can you imagine how you'd say eight hundred and eighty?"

"So what do we conclude as a result?" asked Andrew, frowning.

"Stop being so logical. I'm just agreeing that the way Africans deal with numbers must be different," said David.

"And you agree that Africans are as intelligent as Europeans," Jim prodded.

"Well, it depends on how you define intelligence. Now - " The others yawned ostentatiously

"When you get to Salisbury," Grace told them, "you must contact Judith at the university, for she can show you some of the African schools." Since they were now some days behind schedule, they decided to split up. David would go to Salisbury, while Jim and Andrew would do the local schools. Then they would meet in four days time at Fort Victoria and head for South Africa. This arrangement pleased all three of them - two because they could have more time at Hokonui Ranch, and the third because he rather fancied meeting any daughter of such charismatic parents.

David had had to wrestle with his conscience over staying at the Jamieson Hotel in Salisbury. Loyalty to the code of expeditions would have meant finding somewhere to camp, but he persuaded himself that this would take up too much time, which was becoming a precious commodity. So he forced himself to accept the decadent facilities of civilisation. Somehow he managed to eat the eggs and bacon for breakfast instead of porridge and biscuits, and a bath a day was hideous luxury. Still, he felt less guilty when he thought of the others faring just as well back at Hokonui.

The Faculty of Education at the university had been very helpful, and the Ministry of Education had lent him one of their African messengers (called Faraday) to take him round a couple of schools. The problems here were similar to those in East Africa - particularly the vicious circle of few secondary school places to produce enough teachers for additional secondary schools. In Southern Rhodesia, however, there was less political incentive to improve African education, since white rule was evidently to continue indefinitely. Christian missions did ninety percent of the primary education, and although many, like Dadaya, provided a high standard of teaching, some were mainly concerned with increasing the head-count in their churches, and quantity of pupils took precedent over quality of instruction.

Now he was off to a school in the notorious African suburb of Highfield, where he was to meet Judith, a zealous campaigner for black education. His hair was brushed and his sandals were clean and his heart was beating faster than usual. Judith was even more attractive than he had expected. He shook hands rather clumsily. Judith introduced him to her boyfriend, Graham, to whom David took an instant dislike.

Pat grew crops of tobacco, coffee, cotton and maize in the wonderfully fertile soil of his farm East of Salisbury. His relatives in Sheffield had given his address to David, who called on his way to Fort Victoria. Pat was in the middle of building a new barn, making the bricks himself from a mix of half sand and half anthill. Like everyone else David had recently met, he quickly turned the conversation to politics. Yes, Smith had his complete backing! The local African chiefs would back Smith too - no, they weren't government stooges, but highly respected by the local natives. It was only the nationalist bully-boys from the Salisbury townships who caused trouble, touring the country areas and terrorising the locals. Yes, he knew Africans - he employed dozens - and they didn't want to change government and sink back to poverty.

Pat advised David against sleeping in the open. The main danger, he said, was hyenas. The lack of lions had deprived these scavengers of left-overs, and the owners of the most powerful jaws in the animal kingdom had started doing their own killing, proving both cunning and ruthless. Since one bite could go through a cow's thigh, a man's neck was no problem! David said he would heed the advice, but was too proud to admit that he usually slept inside the Land Rover anyhow. Richard had thought it wimpish. But one day's wimp was another day's survivor. Was it Plato who had said that? Or just Andrew?

Chapter Eleven - South Africa

Andrew and Jim sat on the verandah watching golden birds weaving nests. It had been a wonderful few days - there was a magical poetry about this place. That afternoon a primary school had sung to them - unaccompanied harmony poured forth instinctively it seemed. Andrew had asked what the song was about. "It is a very sad song," a little boy told him, "about a frog and a hippopotamus who fall in love." Andrew had said that he could understand why it might not be a happy situation. Some self-teaching booklets had been tried out on a class of eleven-year-olds, very successfully it appeared. Certainly the comments of the children had been effusive, even ecstatic, but there remained a nagging feeling that the comments were designed chiefly to please the visitors.

The weaver birds fussed round their swinging bundles. The sun was sinking over the Matopa hills and the dry countryside was harshly beautiful. Tomorrow Grace was taking them to see Zimbabwe, the ruined capital of an earlier civilisation, and then on to Fort Victoria to rejoin Charlie. Soon they would leave Springtime in Rhodesia for Autumn in England. For a while they had forgotten to be excited about going home - Africa gripped at something inside you, an unsettling feeling. They had better get home before it grew.

David was looking remarkably neat and well groomed, and Jim wondered if it had anything to do with meeting Judith, but, knowing David's track record, he thought it wouldn't be tactful to ask. Instead they all told each other how terribly hard they had been working, and laughed. Jim drove the first leg towards Beit Bridge. David thought how much better he was looking - was it the Hokonui hospitality or the thought of England in a week's time, he wondered. Lucky Andrew and Jim! How long before he would see England? Two months? Two months more of tedious Programmed Instruction questionnaires, of heat and discomfort and bureaucracy. It made you appreciate England - dappled sunlight on foxgloves beneath the oaks, the sound of wood pigeons, the smell of lawn-cutting in dreamy villages with improbable names like Shingay-cum-Wendy. Whose lousy idea had it been to survey African Education?

A flock of goats wandered across the road in front of them. Different makes of animal had different styles of road use. Sheep and goats meandered in a random sort of way, donkeys tended to stop suddenly in the middle, and the camels of the Middle East had always seemed to plod on remorselessly in a straight line, oblivious of traffic.

As they crossed into South Africa the evening sun was glinting on the Limpopo. The poem was wrong - the river didn't look at all grey-green or greasy. The border-post officials made them take out extra vehicle insurance, which was annoying. They had expected less bureaucracy from white civil servants - let that be punishment for inbuilt prejudice! They headed on South towards Louis Trichardt, whoever he was.

It was nearly dusk when a tyre punctured - the first time that had happened. Ironically, they were on good tarmac at the time, not the rough surfaces Charlie was more used to. They pulled off the road, and parked under a large baobab tree, whose weird root-like branches made you think it had been planted upside-down. Actually, it was a good time to stop for the night, for it was getting hard to see African bicycles, which rarely had lights.

With the wheel changed and supper cooking - rehydrated chow mein had a familiar homely touch after the richer fare of recent days - they turned their thoughts towards tomorrow. They would try to reach Johannesburg well before dusk, to have time to find one of David's tribe of cousins in daylight. Good heavens, this baobab tree would be the site of their last camp! Had they really been on the road for three months? Time was a strange thing. In some ways it seemed only a couple of weeks since they had left England; and yet it was hard to remember life without sleeping bags and the hum of a Land Rover engine. Soon they would be back to newspapers and knowing where you would be next week, exchanging freedom for security. Could you have both? A full moon flooded the bush, and the silence was accentuated, rather than broken, by the occasional call of a plover. Now that was the sound of Africa, and it tugged at something inside them.

After porridge the next morning no one was in a hurry to leave - civilisation was too short a day away. Jim tapped the plaster on his mending arm with his biro, as he searched for the right phrases to bring his diary up to date - he was resisting the urge to ram the biro down inside the plaster and scratch the infuriating itch. Andrew was dozing in the warm sunshine with his back to the baobab. David was prodding his feet with a razor blade. He had been strangely pleased to find a pocket of jigger-flea eggs in a toe, for he remembered his father talking of this occupational hazard of the African bush.

Andrew stretched and started to pack up for the last time. He wondered how Richard was getting on. In a way the Expedition had started to end when Richard had left, he thought, for the team had been broken. Or was it that Charlie had crashed at that point? The mood had certainly become less carefree - not unenjoyable, but more serious somehow, less laughter. Well, a hundred miles to Pietersburg, another two hundred to Johannesburg, and that would be it.

The regimented huts of Soweto spread vastly over the brown land. Jim thought it looked like a concentration camp, but David's Uncle Phil assured him it was better accommodation than the natives were used to. South Africa was a rapidly developing industrial country, and in Johannesburg there were well-paid jobs for Africans, or Bantu as they were termed by the government, provided that they didn't bring their families to live in the White areas.

"Our governing Nationalist Party has, foolishly, made the separation of the races compulsory in law," said Uncle Phil, who was Member of Parliament for the Johannesburg constituency of Kensington, "and this has made us unpopular with the rest of the world. But the races have always tended to live in separate areas anyhow, for their life-styles would not be comfortable close together. The United Party, to which I belong, opposes Apartheid, but accepts that it will be a long time before Africans and Europeans can be treated as equals."

Jim winced. "How long?" he asked.

"It depends on education for one thing," said Uncle Phil. "We spend far more per head on Bantu education than other African countries do."

"To be educated sufficiently for manual labourers?" asked Jim acidly.

"There are universities, too, for Blacks and Coloureds."

"But," broke in Andrew, "they will remain second-class citizens of their own country!" Uncle Phil smiled - he loved a good argument.

"Let's disagree on matters of opinion, but facts are different - it is no more the Blacks' country than it is the Whites'! When the Dutch were landing at the Cape in the mid sixteen-hundreds, the Bantu people were coming down into the North-east of the country. You could say the country *belonged to* the Hottentots and Bushmen at that time, but these former inhabitants were virtually eradicated by the incomers, black and white, just like the North American Indians or the Australian Aborigines were by you English!"

"Let's forget the ancient history and stick to the present situation," Jim put in. "How can you deny some of the human beings who share the country a voice in running the country?"

"Because they are not ready for it. Oh, there are some wonderful Africans - I get on well with them. I met with Chief Albert Luthuli only the other day - he's one of the Black leaders and a charming man, but not capable of running a country."

"They are running their own countries in East Africa!"

"Ah, but wait a while. You've seen the standard of education in those countries - how long will they be able to cope for themselves? Britain has done this continent no favours by dropping its colonies like hot bricks. When your Harold Macmillan came here and told us that 'a wind of change is blowing through Africa' it was clear he was going to sell the Whites down the river! If Britain really wanted to be altruistic, it would have stayed in Africa and educated Africans."

They were still arguing ("no, discussing!" said Uncle Phil) when they got back to Maisie's. Maisie was Uncle Phil's daughter, with whom the Expedition was staying for the last couple of days before the 'plane to England. David was there ahead of them, nonchalantly sipping fruit juice by the swimming pool like a colonial grandee. He was surrounded by an attendant court of Maisie's small children, who regarded their scruffy visitors with great respect - nay, awe!

"I found the travel agent," he said, "and the Straat Franklin sails for Nigeria in a fortnight. I'll load Charlie at Capetown before getting my flight to Ghana. By then you poor suckers will be slaving back in the English smog !" He didn't feel quite so relaxed about going solo as he hoped he sounded. Not that he *needed* their support, of course, but it was always nice to have someone to whom you could say "Isn't that a great sight?" or "Doesn't the bureaucracy make you puke!" or some other erudite comment.

Maisie put her head out of the wisteria round the window to say she had booked seats for the tribal dancing display that evening at one of the gold mines. Jim and Andrew weren't sure whether attendance might be tacit support of apartheid, but it would have been rude to refuse, so they went - and almost enjoyed it. The infectious enthusiasm of the dancers, the colourful costumes, the rhythm and teamwork, all made them want to celebrate African culture and tradition. But all the time they were reminded of the structure of South African society. For one thing, all the dancers were very black and all the audience was very white. For another thing, there were no women dancing, their roles being performed by men wearing dresses (and looking slightly uncomfortable) - the law required womenfolk to be left back in the tribal homeland while their men worked in Johannesburg.

"It's a very vibrant display!" said David, being polite to a lady sitting next to him. "Yees, the Blicks have rhythm," she agreed, and went on to tell him that the various tribal groups would gladly kill each other if they could. "The Zulus and the Xhosa have to have different days off, else they would fight," she said. "They hate each other far more than they hate us."

"You chaps on holiday?" asked the man sitting next to her.

"Not really. We're doing an educational survey."

"Oh!" said the man, "students on a joy-ride."

"No," interjected Andrew, who had overheard, "it's been hard work actually. We've been to dozens of schools in several countries."

"Yes?" said the man in a bored sort of voice. "And what have you discovered that's new?"

"That's not the point," said David, frowning. "It's a case of bringing information together, to help design teaching methods."

"And who's going to use this information?"

"UNESCO - probably," said David, beginning to feel less sure now that he thought about it.

"Probably sit on a shelf in someone's office," grunted the man, who clearly had had some experience of surveys.

"Don't be so hard on the boys," said the woman. "It's a good way to see a bit of the world before they start proper work." David's mouth opened and then shut again - he would think of a devastating reply in about an hour's time.

The Expedition's last day in Jo'burg had a funny limbo feeling about it, neither one thing nor the other, because you couldn't really concentrate on Africa when your plane was shortly to leave for home. However, Andrew and Jim were doing their best to help David plan his future schedule, about which he seemed a bit vague. This was partly because the forward planning had been less thorough for the Expedition's later stages - with so much uncertainty about timing, it had to be - and partly because David thought the others must be bitterly disappointed to miss out on delivering Charlie to the Mission, and didn't want to rub it in by talking about Nigeria. But he didn't tell them what he was thinking, and they didn't actually say they were worried about how he would manage on his own. The conversation was a bit stilted, and they all felt rather awkward.

Andrew looked across the breakfast-table and thought how much they would miss all this gorgeous fruit! Nora, the Xhosa housegirl, came in with bacon and eggs. David couldn't help feeling that the other two would be uncomfortable to be waited on by Blacks, and hoped that his cousins wouldn't notice it. He felt his loyalties divided between friends and family; so he made loud "enjoying my food" noises to cover his embarrassment.

They took the smaller cousins to a gymnastics display that morning, as a sort of thank-you gesture. Andrew feared it would be a rather tedious duty - but it turned out to be quite enjoyable (the schoolgirl gymnasts taking part were much better developed than their English counterparts). Then Jim and Andrew spent the afternoon packing, while David went to buy himself a suit. Maisie had been quite firm about that - she didn't want the family let down when he went to meet educationalists! He came back complaining that it had cost eleven pounds.

How do you say goodbye to someone with whom you have literally rubbed shoulders for three months? David was wondering about this as he drove the others to the Airport Bus at five-thirty next morning. The roads were wet and there was a cold wind; it seemed that the British climate was coming to meet them. "Pity you can't take the surplus cheese with you!" he said. What a vacuous remark, he thought.

"We never used Charlie's winch!" said Andrew.

"It would have been useful if we had gone through the Sahara," said Jim. Cases were loaded; the bus engine started.

"Why did you say 'donkey manure' to that man?" frowned Andrew.

"It means 'thank you sir' in Afrikaans," replied David.

They shook hands - how ridiculously British!

"Have a good journey!"

"And you!"

And they were gone.

David put on his new suit and drove over to the Johannesburg Educational Research Institute, where his contact, a tall, burly man with a guttural Afrikaans accent, worked on self-teaching materials for South African schools. Over coffee he asked defensively what David thought of their politics, and, without waiting for a reply, explained that no one would understand South Africa until they realised that the Boers believed they had a sacred duty to impose civilisation on the country. It was a religious thing, he said, and world opinion was of little consequence. He kindly arranged three days of visits - to a College of Education, the Anglo American mine training centre, and the Department of Bantu Education.

It was at the latter that a note of discord arose. It was certainly not all his fault, David thought afterwards, but perhaps he could have been more tactful. Everything started well enough: David had been flattered to be met by a senior official, and got off on the right foot by saying that he understood that more was spent on Black education here than in the countries to the North. The official, a plump middle-aged Afrikaaner with heavy eyebrows, cold eyes and a twitch, smiled in an unctuous sort of way. Then, for some reason, David put in - a sort of aside, really - that it was still a lot less, presumably, than was spent on White education. And that started it. Evidently his host was sensitive on the point, for he came back quite sharply to say that

Whites contributed a considerable amount to Black Education, while Blacks contributed nothing to White education. David said he could understand that, and the man seemed somewhat mollified. But David added something about not being able to contribute much if you weren't given much, and the atmosphere deteriorated.

"The education of twelve million Bantu by three million Whites is a heavy burden," frowned the man. "We tax the Bantu very leniently - only three and a half Rand annually per adult male - and less than half of this is collected because of defaulters, against whom little drastic action is taken! And everything raised from Bantu tax goes to Bantu education!" His voice was rising in pitch and volume. "In addition, White taxpayers contribute over twelve million Rand a year to Bantu schools! Some would say that this is more than generous - some would say that the various ethnic groups should pay for their own education!"

"Right," said David, thinking he had better move to other topics on his questionnaire, "and what are the objectives of Bantu education?" The official's eyes retreated under his eyebrows.

"What do you mean by that?" he asked suspiciously.

"Well, what role for the African does the education system assume?" It was an honest attempt to clarify the term 'objective', but clearly seemed to touch a raw nerve.

"I think you are referring to the common allegation that Bantu education is angled towards producing workers for lower positions in industry?"

"Well, no, not really. I'm asking what Bantu education fits people for," said David, trying to sound friendly and reasonable.

"Exactly!" snorted the official triumphantly. "We are used to insinuations that this Department is a means of ensuring White supremacy! Because we educate the Bantu to serve their own people, you think the education is inferior? Let me tell you that the Bantu are trained for nearly all occupations found in a civilised community, and when I say 'trained' I don't mean just training in manual skills. No, I include the _onderwys_ as well as the _onderichte_, producing Black university professors as well as Black tradesmen, taught by Black teachers to serve the Black homelands!" He had become quite animated, stressing each point by pounding the table.

"Splendid," murmured David nervously.

"Now, any other questions?" said the man, breathing heavily. David tried to collect his thoughts; he felt he was losing ground, and wished that Jim or Andrew were there - they would have probed incisively at the weak points in the official's position. What would they have asked? After all, he had a sort of duty to express the views of absent members of the Expedition, hadn't he?

"The native reserves you speak of......"

"Bantu homelands."

"The Bantu homelands you speak of, are they to be governed democratically?"

"The people will have self-determination, like the Transkei already has."

"But they will have to fit in with the government of the surrounding White areas?"

"We will have to learn to live together, yes." He gave a sort of half smile, but it may have been a twitch, it was hard to tell.

"So," said David, feeling like the prosecuting attorney in an American movie, "it is necessary for the Bantu to accept the system of Apartheid and..."

"The policy of Separate Development is in their own interest." Big twitch.

"And therefore Bantu education presumably includes material to teach the Blacks that Apartheid is in their own interest?" The District Attorney allowed himself a moment of quiet satisfaction, for the Official definitely seemed taken aback.

"I think you are suggesting that our syllabus is politically angled?"

"Yes." - Oh dear, that was a mistake, he had fallen for the leading question. Why had he said 'yes'? He knew nothing of the Bantu syllabus. He should be asking, not suggesting, and felt he had put himself in the wrong. The Official was twitching in a big way now. His voice became harsh.

"Do you expect me to refute wild and sweeping statements of that nature?" David felt himself colouring. It was all Andrew's and Jim's fault - they shouldn't have influenced him so much.

"It's comparable," said the Official, now recovering his poise, "it's comparable to asking your London Education Authority whether they indoctrinate their pupils with socialist ideas!"

"But they do!" said David, indignantly.

The interview was evidently over. David found himself thanking the Official for seeing him. He was angry with himself for getting political when he should have been coolly objective. He had let himself be sucked into a contest, and what really hurt was somehow losing when he had been about to win.

Chapter Twelve - Basutoland to Ghana

Dear Jim and Andrew and Richard,

Dusk is settling on Maseru, capital of the British Protectorate of Basutoland. It's the eighth of October, and we find our intrepid explorer sitting on a hillside, contemplating the peaceful scene. Maseru is an unassuming little town for a capital, but let not appearances deceive - it has just begun its own parliament, and is opening a new university (well, renaming the College of Education). Both these big events are being rather hurried, so as to be in time for - yes, you've guessed it - Independence. Well, why should Basutoland miss out on the spirit of the decade? Particularly since it has regarded itself as a bit apart ever since the locals appealed to Queen Victoria to save them from absorption by the surrounding South Africa, and she obliged.

Since they depend for most things on their big neighbour, it was not surprising that an erstwhile South African MP was selected to be the first Speaker of the new House of Representatives, with the mission of inculcating the ethos of parliamentary democracy. He is the image of an English Colonel, brusque and military, but quite a nice man behind the facade. Uncle Phil gave me his address, so I dropped round at lunchtime, and his wife kindly asked me to stay and eat. I was on my best behaviour, don't worry. My manners didn't falter even when the Colonel told me his father-in-law was a Don at Oxford - no corny comments, no; I nodded affably and said I had heard of the place.

The main problem in establishing parliamentary procedures here, the Speaker tells me, is getting the Basutos to accept the principle of compromise. Evidently it is traditional to regard agreement - on anything - as a sign of weakness, and debates tend to be lengthy wars of attrition from entrenched positions. Another difficult concept is neutrality. They are reluctant to accept that The Speaker must be unbiased, being convinced that self-interest is the only reasonable motive for behaviour. Maybe their understanding of human nature is more advanced than was thought.

I left Johannesburg yesterday evening with a parting gift of fruit drops from the little cousins, and sucked my way as far as Winsburg before stopping in the early hours for sleep. You can't really pitch camp in a suit, so I stayed at a seedy motel, from which departure at dawn was a pleasure. Thence it was only a couple of hours driving through rolling pastureland to Maseru. The overworked staff at the tiny Ministry of Education didn't seem too pleased to be distracted from organising the new university, particularly by anyone with UNESCO connections (a UNESCO report had just given their Secondary Education a drubbing). However, exuding ostentatious humility, I was able to ascertain that most children attended Primary school some of the time, that the pupil-teacher ratio was sixty to one, and that two thirds of teachers had been trained.

What did I say about the gentle peace of evening? A huge thunder storm is now heading across the hills towards me, so I shall retreat smartly to the security of Charlie. Someone told me that you are safe from lightning strikes inside a vehicle, since electric charge remains on the outside of a hollow container. I'm sure they are right.

The Basuto educational system is run by the churches, under loose government supervision, and I am visiting a school at Teyateyaneng (understandably abbreviated to TY). TY isn't that far from Maseru - on the map - but it took several hours to wind up and down various passes and valleys to get here. The route to St. Agnes' Mission may be tortuous, but it was sheer pleasure to travel through the stunning mountain scenery. Brother Chris, an Australian monk, told me that the mission's UK headquarters once queried his petrol expenses for the Maseru to TY trip, pointing out the short distance "as the crow flies". He wrote back that no crows were available!

I was invited to TY by Father Anthony, whom I met in Sheffield last year. I've brought with me the books he wanted on "do-it-yourself" Programming. But I remind him that they were written for England - and Africa is different. What Europeans understand from pictures, for example, may not be the same as Africans do. A recent African birth-control campaign in Johannesburg failed for this reason. Posters had shown two families, one with two well-fed, well-dressed, smiling children, the other with ten thin unhappy children. It had a great effect, and people poured into the family-planning clinics - to ask how they could get big families "like the man in the picture"!

I have been given a pleasant guest-room, and told that I needn't attend any of the services during the night! After supper, I am to address the teaching staff on "Programming" (the tame expert role!). ✴ I'll tell them that the technique works, but is no panacea, that it's useful but won't solve the shortage of human teachers - that it's a teaching aid rather than a teacher replacement.

The Great Karroo - it sounds like a prehistoric flesh-eater or an Italian tenor - stretches vastly on either side of the straight, straight road. You would have thought they could have introduced a few unnecessary corners just for interest - didn't they make Dinky Tracks in their school playgrounds? Occasionally the brown flatness is relieved by a few thousand acres of yellow flowers, triggered by a Spring shower, but most of the time there's little to keep a driver awake. I've sang all the Welsh Methodist hymns I know and I've recited Hiyawatha (but "Oh, the long and dreary winter, oh the cold and cruel winter" doesn't sound right in the middle of sun-baked scrub). It's very hot in the Land Rover, and opening the windows serves only to pump in more heat. What can I think about next?

One of these days I would like to go back to Basutoland. The mountains have a sort of peaceful clarity that puts the world into perspective. Driving back from TY on the steep dirt roads yesterday, I passed flocks of sheep tended by boys standing on one leg and wrapped in colourful blankets - just like the travel posters. The little Basuto villages had a smattering of the round thatched roofs that are another feature of travel brochures, although most of the houses are square and roofed with corrugated iron (photographers must be careful where they point their lenses). Most of the treeless land is pasture, but I did see a team of oxen ploughing a patch of arable farmland. Because there are no tsetse fly up there, horses and cattle thrive.

A bridge back into the Orange Free State was guarded by a solitary Basuto soldier, who asked no question and wanted to see no passport. Would that all borders were as relaxed! You know how tired we got of border posts - embodying the worst in officialdom, with small authority clad in mental jackboots. I'm getting tired of travelling between border posts, too! Still, only a few weeks to go. Oh, look! On the left there - a pile of rocks! That was nice.

Tomorrow I'm due in Capetown, and looking forward to seeing Uncle Phil again - Parliament has moved down from Pretoria for the Summer. I'm not going to apologise for being a fan of my uncle! Did I tell you his history? It's like something out of Boy's Own - brought up in a small fishing town; scholarship to Liverpool University; won the North of England Mile Championship in 1911; badly wounded in 1916 with the Rhodesian mounted infantry in East Africa; then a school inspector; became President of the South African Stock Exchange; then Member of Parliament - you name it, he's done it! But when you're with him you forget to be overwhelmed, for he always seems so interested in what you are doing and in your opinions. You find yourself talking while he listens. A man for all seasons! All right, I know I'm biased!

Charlie has started the descent to the coastal plain at last. We pass an impressive series of warning notices: "Dangerous Bend Two Miles Ahead", "Slow Down, Dangerous Bend One Mile Ahead", "No, much slower than that! Bend in Half a Mile!", "Even slower! Bend Quarter Mile Ahead!", "Now SLOW DOWN some more!"; by the time you crawl round the corner it seems relatively tame. Before the signs were erected there used to be countless fatalities at that corner (the first really sharp one after hundreds of miles of straight road).

It's raining heavily as Worcester approaches, and the traffic is really heavy. I think I prefer the Great Karroo. I'm tired and need to hand over the wheel, but there is no one to take it now. To think that we used to compete for turns at driving!

I'm having lunch at Newlands, a suburb of Capetown, with a couple who, after half a century here, still have vestiges of Scots accents. The Senator is a small man, with egg on his tie. "You've spilt again, William!" his wife scolds. He smiles gently, and resumes telling me how he was a jockey in the Cheltenham Gold Cup in 1910. "Then I got a job as organiser with the Trade Union Movement, who sent me to South Africa in 1912 to organise Trade Unions for the Black Miners. I've been trying for over fifty years!" He shakes his head sadly. Until the Nat. Government abolished the system in 1960, he represented Black South Africans in the Senate, while his wife, Margaret, represented Cape Province Blacks in the House of Assembly. Margaret is deep in political discussion with Uncle Phil. When she was leader of the South African Liberal Party they were close colleagues in the fight to improve educational facilities for non-whites.

"I enjoy a trip back to England," continues William, "particularly the race meetings! I bought a new car on the proceeds last time. But you must never bet heavily on any one race, no matter how sure you are. Frequent modest wins - that's the way. Don't you agree, Dear?" His wife looks up. "Do be quiet, William. I'm talking with Philip."

"She's got a brilliant mind," he says, taking me out into the garden. "She was the first girl to win the Port Elizabeth matriculation gold medal!" Above us Table Mountain towers over the rocky, wooded slopes.

"She's just finished a year at Nuffield College, Oxford, writing a book on the history of Apartheid," he says proudly.

Simonstown is more like a Cornish fishing village than the Headquarters of the South African navy. I've spent a fairly tedious morning hearing about their use of Programmed Instruction, and now the Commander in charge of training is giving me lunch in the Officers' Mess. He's a nice chap, but the conversation is flagging - there is only so much you can say about Programmed Instruction. In an effort to diversify proceedings, I comment on the visit of a senior Israeli politician, mentioned on the radio news this morning. Then I hear myself saying "I suppose that's in connection with your nuclear project?". Why don't I keep my big mouth shut? There is a sudden silence throughout the room.

"What nuclear project?" asks the Commander in staccato.

"Well, I just thought - since they have the scientists and you have the uranium ....and both of you have hostile neighbours ....well, I just wondered if perhaps you were getting together....." Somehow I don't think I would be a great success in the diplomatic service. Lunch undergoes a marked acceleration, and I'm driving back to Capetown. Oh well, I wanted to be back early in any case. I've got to go to the docks, where the shipping agents Quick and Louw (sound like Welsh rugby players) will look after Charlie until the Straat

Franklin sails for Lagos tomorrow. I give Charlie a pat and say that I'll see him in a fortnight.

I am seen off at Malan Airport by Uncle Phil and the Senator and his wife. The South African Airways mechanics' strike is over just in time for my flight to Johannesburg. "We are getting as bad as Britain for strikes!" smiles Margaret, to fill the painful silence while you are waiting for someone to go. The DC7 takes three hours to fly from Capetown, and then I board a Pan Am Clipper Jet for the weekly flight to Ghana.

This first time on a jet is really exciting! To fly at 575 miles an hour at 32,000 feet is amazing! South Africa soon slips away beneath the wing and we are over brown Bechuanaland - that must be the Kalahari. Now we're over Angola, I think. Big place, Africa, but jets make it seem manageable. How different from the Thirties, when my father took a week to fly from Jo'burg to England, landing every night (so as not to get lost), during the day landing every hour or two for meals, or to refuel, or to avoid thunder storms!

Six miles below, the scrub thickens. It looks greener and the clearings are getting smaller. Will that be the Congo? What a mess the civil war is making of that country! Violence has always seemed endemic in Africa. Come to think of it, in Europe, too, so I mustn't get bumptious. But Africa seems to indulge in it with fewer inhibitions somehow. We are now coming in to land at Leopoldville. I wonder how long it would have taken to drive here?

A couple of giant US Airforce freighters are parked some distance from the terminal, surrounded by a litter of lounging US Marines, rifles slung from shoulders and jaws chewing incessantly. A Belgian, drinking coffee alongside me, says that they are here to train the government forces, but only because the Communists support the other side. A propellored fighter takes off for a rocket attack on the rebels to the East. Our fuelling stop is over and we reboard. It is humid and overcast at ground level, but as we climb above the rippled sea of cloud the sunset hits us, and the whole horizon is painted orange.

"But I was told that British citizens didn't require a visa!"

"Usually that is so, Sah, but you have come from South Africa, so you need one to enter the country."

"But I don't have one! So what am I supposed to do?" The Ghanaian official shrugs his shoulders. Don't say I'm to be sent back!

"Can I help?" says an English voice at my shoulder. "I'm from the British Council. We are expecting you, I think." He looks at the passport on the Immigration Officer's desk. "Yes, " he says to the official, "UNESCO Representative, guest of the British Council, I'll look after it." And he takes my arm and sweeps me through the formalities. What a splendid institution this British Council is!

Outside the airport a sensible Ford Zephyr is waiting, and we drive through the darkness to Legon University, a few miles outside Accra. The B.C. has arranged for me to stay there in a "Fellow's Flat", and very comfortable it is - makes rooms at Emmanuel seem downmarket!

Different countries have different names for the strip where you walk alongside the road - sidewalk, pavement, parapet, footpath - and in this city that strip is made of earth and rubble. You have to watch your footing lest you trip into the open drain next to it, the stench from which makes Middle Eastern sanitation seem advanced. I'm starting to sound like a tedious Colonialist, so I'd better not complain about the steamy heat, nor the mealie gruel for breakfast (the coffee and rolls were very good). A British Council car collected me - isn't the B.C. wonderful? - and I have just finished a two-hour briefing with their Representative, as the top man is called. Now I'm sampling Accra. First things first, where do I find an English newspaper?

Accra seems a more primitive capital than the East African ones. There is the occasional big store, but most of the buildings are in the rickety category. Eventually I find a paper. It's a week old, but the Labour victory in the UK elections is news to me. It's a small majority, but I know that it will please Jim, who is going through the normal healthy socialist phase. As for me, I will take what comfort I can from a continuing small Liberal presence, and mouth comforting platitudes like 'bread needs a little yeast'. I wonder what party is in power here? A local paper has a front page feature on Kwame Nkrumah, "His Messianic Dedication". The title seems somewhat excessive for a democratic country! It looks like power is not so much in the hands of a party as in the hands of an individual. Still, this is now an independent country and must work out its own system, I suppose.

It is hot and clammy and crowded. I wonder if the teeming throng around me care much about who is in power, so long as they have food and family. The street is full of noise and colour. To move you jostle. West Africa is supposed to be the least healthy spot on Earth, but there are an awful lot of survivors. Now, individuals are lovely; but a few thousand of them can be less so. It would be nice to be able to retreat to peace and quiet, but there is no Land Rover parked round the corner, and I feel vulnerable. I think of Charlie plodding up the South Atlantic and wonder if he is missing me. Stop being so foolish - he's a machine. Sorry - it's a machine! Good heavens, you can't get emotionally attached to a machine, now can you? That would be silly.

It's time to set out for my afternoon appointments. The British Council, to whom be praise, have lined up the UNESCO Chief of Mission here and the Minister of Education. I hope they realise that I'm merely a first-year research student and not a world expert!

It's "High Table" night at Legon University. All wear gowns and stand when the Top Table enters. Grace is said before the spiced meat and mashed yams. Thereafter it is a bit like the Rugby Club Dinner at Emmanuel, with a good deal of cheering and banging and shouting. That must be Conor Cruse O'Brien up there; I think he's the vice-chancellor here, after his spell with the United Nations in the Congo. Should I wander over and say "Thanks for having me", or "Sorry you couldn't sort out the Congo"? Maybe not - he might ask how sorting out African Education is going!

I'm sitting with Winston, a Ghanaian student from the rooms next to mine, and an American Negro (is that the polite term, or should one say 'Black'?) who is on a year's exchange course. He is telling us about his subject, the old Ghana empire. Evidently, a few hundred years ago it extended over a vast swathe of West Africa, from Morocco to the Congo, fuelled by trade in salt and gold and ivory. It had the sense to avoid fixed boundaries, and just adapted its size to the trading alliances of the moment; which saved the huge trouble of bickering over borders. Our American friend is researching its trade links with the Americas in the twelfth century! The theory is that large dug-out canoes travelled with the South Atlantic current to the East coast of what is now USA, long before Columbus, and returned with the Gulf Stream. When I expressed polite incredulity, I was told there are records of such canoes being shipwrecked in Holland on the way back.

This afternoon I met the local Anglican Bishop. I was given his address by Father Anthony at TY, who said he was worth a visit. How true, the Bishop was a mine of information on local education. What's more, he used to be in Sheffield - not being intellectual in the refined university area but organising youth clubs in the rough lands. He told me that the way he judged the success of a Saturday night was by the number of puddles on the floor - if the film was really good, they didn't want to go out and miss any of it! The Bishop has a rather neat way of assessing when a newly independent country reaches maturity - it's when the blame for a problem is laid on their own people, instead of wicked colonialists.

I'm going to move to a modest Accra hotel in the morning. It just takes too long getting back and forth to Legon - besides, tomorrow's menu is curried fish and yams for lunch and curried omelette for dinner. Local culture needs to be experienced in moderation.

The British Council Zephyr with the slipping clutch is taking me to a teacher training college in Winneba, forty miles away. The African driver, Philip, weaves between the Mammy Wagons, those trucks that carrying anything and everybody, emblazoned with painted titles and texts ("Wisdom", "Te Deum laudamus", "Money is root of evil" and even "Patience", which is something that the drivers certainly don't have). Pedestrians intermingle with the traffic. Philip strikes one a glancing blow - "He's fine," he laughs, "look, he's running away!" Further on, a group of inebriated women are helping each other remain upright by the roadside. "They've probably been to a funeral," Philip explains.

I'm supposed to be gauging the effect of a recent UNESCO Workshop which dealt with Programmed Instruction. The great need is for people to write material for use in schools, but attendance at

UNESCO conferences is a kudos thing, so most of the participants were senior administrators without the time or inclination to actually produce teaching booklets. I meet the Ministry of Education man in charge of preparing Programmes to teach the Decimal Coinage system, who doesn't think Programmed Instruction is much use. I fear the failure of his project will support his view.

The Avenida Hotel is not cheap, nor does it have any hot water; but at least it is in downtown Accra. It also arranges for the guests' shoes to be cleaned overnight - it was quite a surprise to find my suedes liberally coated with brown polish. Steady! I mustn't complain like a boring Colonialist! Look on the bright side - the place has tablecloths in the dining room (with the water shortage, you can't expect them to be clean) and there's real linoleum in the bedrooms. The shopping centre is nearby, but the shops have little to sell. Imports have been severely curtailed because foreign currency is needed to pay for the Volta Dam project. It is most fortunate that His Messianic Dedication's Palace was completed before the restrictions. I went past it yesterday - a huge complex, half fortress and half Hilton, overlooking the coastal plain.

I've managed to get a flight to Nigeria a couple of days earlier than originally planned. I hope no one thinks I'm fed up with this place - heaven forbid! It's just that I've done all my list of visits, and I want to be sure to get to Lagos before the Straat Franklin arrives with Charlie.

The last day in Ghana. This morning I went to the Bishop's Accra primary schools, one boys' and one girls', and they were impressive. It quite cheered me up to find dedicated and competent teachers; maybe there is hope for education here. But then I went to the Ministry of Education for some reports they had promised me, and nobody could find them. I must correct the previous paragraph - I admit I'm fed up with the place. I wonder if Nigeria will be better.

I think the plane is about to leave, because, although there has been no announcement on the loudspeaker, people are heading for the door and making for a Ghana Airways plane. It's probably a cunning plot to make the wicked colonialists miss their flight. I join the throng and hope we are going to Lagos. Now I'm wedged in the doorway between two large ladies with piles of saucepans on their heads. After you, Madam. Maybe I should not have been chivalrous, for now my seat number is occupied by a woman with two babies slung from her neck. I look for another one. It's not easy - there seem far fewer seats than people. Wait, there's one empty at the back, but I'm not the only one that's noticed. My relative youth enables me to outpace the competition. No, I won't give it up! Well, tough! This wicked colonialist is not moving. You should have a more organised airline. An elderly lady in the next seat watches me impassively and chews. Yes, of course I'll hold your bucket for you - it's only an hour's flight after all. She smiles, and spits - probably a local gesture of esteem.

Thank goodness the plane has four engines; if one goes wrong we'll still have three left. It's getting dark outside. Those dots of light below must be Dahomey - or Togo? French territories I think, with wonderfully straight borders, following some European administrator's pencil line. Now we're losing height. I hope it's because they've found an airport. Wouldn't it be nice if it was Lagos?

Chapter Thirteen - Nigeria

The rain is pounding on the metal roof and water is pouring in. I've pushed old socks into most of the cracks, but still it comes. What the people between Ilesha and Benin City have done to deserve such a thunder storm I don't know, but I wish I wasn't in the middle of it. Poor Charlie has had a few gaps at the corners since rolling around the ditches of Northern Rhodesia, and these sheets of water are finding them. You can't drive in this deluge, so I've pulled off the road. In any case it's getting late, so I'll have a bottle of coke and a tin of spam. If you open a sealed container there is less chance of suffering gut-rot (the Expedition's hygiene regulations haven't changed!). Afterwards I'll bale out the Land Rover and sleep on the sodden front seats - no way am I going to step outside into a night like this. Be blowed to any notion of hardy explorers!

It was so good to leave Lagos this morning. African bureaucracy can leave any travel schedule in tatters, and it has taken nearly a week to free Charlie from the grasp of the Apapa Wharf customs sheds. I think I would still be there were it not for Tiny. Tiny is a very large man, as his name implies to anyone from an English Public School. He is one of the few remaining ex-pats still in Nigerian employ - and he goes in a month's time. Thank goodness I got here before he does, because he is Commander of the Preventative Section of the Board of Customs, no less, and wields influence. A retired teacher whom I consulted before leaving England told me that one should seek Tiny's assistance if one were in difficulty. One was, and one did.

The Straat Franklin arrived in Lagos a couple of days after I did, and I went to the docks to greet Charlie. I had spent the previous day trying to find various "clearance papers" that Holland West African Line should have sent to my poste restante at the Bank of West Africa in Lagos. Thither I had gone, to find that nobody knew anything about my poste restante, let alone Charlie's documents. We hardened travellers know that, faced with officialdom, it is fatal to show weakness. So, if unsure of one's ground, the recommended tactic is to shout. This I did, demanding to see the manager immediately. The clerk in front of me wilted visibly and trotted off with a heavy sigh - I felt a cad, but one cannot be squeamish in emergencies. He returned shortly to say that the manager was at the lavatory. I hesitated for a moment, not having come across the lavatory counterploy before, but covered quickly with an understanding nod and a declaration of intent to remain blocking the head of the queue until the manager had finished. The queue-blocking move is not without risk, because of the hostility engendered fore and aft, but on this occasion it produced the Nigerian manager remarkably quickly, who shamed me by being quietly charming. He telephoned round and found my poste restante at the Marina branch, and then to my embarrassment insisted on providing a car to take me there. I felt rather small, and regretted that Ghana had sullied my opinion of West Africans.

The mail was very welcome. There were exhortations from Aunt Madge about eating plenty of vegetables, and reminders from Mother about airing clothes properly, but nothing whatsoever from shipping agents - not one solitary scrap of "clearance" paper that would help release Charlie. It was at this point that I sought out Tiny. He was that morning much exercised by the Fernando Po situation. This off-shore island (nominally Spanish I think) specialises in smuggling into the Cross River estuary near Calabar, using sea-going canoes with powerful outboard engines. Tiny's fast launches are a match for any of them, but the one stationed off the Cross River had just been towed into port with a seized engine (a case of forgetting to check the oil). Tiny's man on Fernando Po had reported that, on receipt of telegrams reporting this event, every available canoe had set off, loaded to the gunwales with contraband. I was grateful that, in the midst of the Preventative Section's anguish, he found time to write a letter to the authorities at Apapa Wharf, requesting every assistance to release Charlie. I hate privilege and special treatment, even more a system that requires them, but Charlie had sailed from South Africa (that hated bastion of Apartheid) so the odds were stacked against us, and I needed any help going.

Charlie sat forlornly in the middle of the vast Customs shed, surrounded by bales and crates and clutter and strange smells.

"I've come to collect the Land Rover, if I may."

"No papers? Embarked in Capetown? No release!"

"I have a letter........" and handed it to the glowering African official. There was a huddle of customs officers and much whispering - then a flurry of salutes and it was suddenly a different world. Uniforms flocked to offer advice, Charlie was admired, forms were filled in for me. Finally, the Collector of Customs appeared in person to announce that everything was now in order except an import permit, which was beyond his control. I would have to approach the Minister of Trade, he said, and his expression suggested it wouldn't be easy.

Nor was it. Particularly if you didn't want to pay import duty, which was more than I or the Mission Hospital could afford. But the System required import duty if a vehicle was to be left in the country. The regulations were quite clear and quite simple, and quite easy for a Ministry of Trade civil servant to point out to a sweaty youth who had an irrational expectation that the System could be flexible. I argued black and blue (if you'll forgive the mention of colour) that there must be means of making an exception if the vehicle was a gift to the Nigerian people, that it was for helping the sick, that in any case it was rather battered so not worth much, that I wasn't feeling very well, and that I could readily burst into tears if that would help. All to no avail. The System was impregnable. After a long, long day wrestling with bureaucracy (in short bursts with long waits between while relays of fresh officials were found to explain why it wasn't possible) I gave up on the Ministry of Trade. Tiny suggested that the Finance Ministry might be able to over-rule Trade, so I fixed up an appointment for the next day.

I suppose I must have seemed pretty depressed, for Tiny insisted I came to supper. His wife is a real sweetie, and a pretty good cook. She teaches at a local African primary school, and told me how hunger was a greater concern than teaching methods in her class. On the way back Tiny showed me round Lagos. At one stage I commented on a most impressive mansion we were passing.

"It belongs to the Minister of Finance," said Tiny. "Cost nearly a million pounds."

"He must get a huge salary!"

"No, just the usual cabinet rate."

"How can he afford a house like that?"

"That's what many people wonder!"

I waited patiently most of the next morning in the antechambers of the Ministry of Finance. Eventually I found myself in the office of the Deputy Permanent Secretary, and - joy oh joy - he was wonderfully helpful. When you are tired and hot and cross, and you find someone who says "I think it can be done" you bestow your esteem on his race, be it British, African or Chinese. This paragon of sense and sensibility happened to be British. If I think therefore that the British are superior, I should not be accused of racism or prejudice, because prejudice is irrational, and my views are grounded on dispassionate evidence. I suppose I could be accused of basing my opinion on too small a sample, but that does not mean it is false. Enough of abstract wanderings!

My Deputy Permanent Secretary had been kept on for a year or two after Independence "to effect a smooth transition of administration". A cynic, and I fear I'm becoming one, might say it was to postpone the shambles to come.

"It will take a week or two," the neat little man told me, "but here's a temporary permit in the meantime. While you deliver the vehicle to Eastern Nigeria, I'll see if the Minister will waive import duty. Call on your way back through Lagos." I could have kissed him! But we British don't display emotion, so I shook his hand (very warmly, let it be said). At the risk of offending the purists further, Hooray for the British!

I did more that afternoon than I had done in the previous week. I collected Charlie, took the boxes of completed questionnaires down to the Elder-Dempster warehouse (I'm on the boat to Liverpool in a fortnight), delivered the surplus food in Charlie to the school where Tiny's wife teaches, and, finally, bought a watch. The latter was sort of accidental, really, but this Nigerian followed me down the street offering "Swiss watches" at four pounds ten shillings. The poor chap did not know that I had been trained by Richard, and three streets later the transaction was completed for one pound ten shillings. I wonder how long before it goes wrong?

Having had little success finding the teachers interested in Programmed Instruction with addresses in the Lagos area, I stopped on my way through Ibadan this morning to see a contact at the Ministry of Education offices there. He couldn't be found, apologised his deputy, a nice little man who tried to be helpful. I think that I would normally have been grateful and polite, but, to my dismay, I heard myself telling him that he was useless, that his Department was useless, and that I was fed up with his whole stinking country. The heat and humidity were very poor excuses for my behaviour, and as I drove East on the ploughed tarmac to Ife I had to admit that I really didn't like the person I was becoming. Or, I wondered, had I always been that person and had concealed it until now? Surely it must be a temporary aberration! I'm sure I'm not like that. Not really. It must be Africa's fault!

I thought I was driving pretty fast, but the Mammy wagons, bulging with goods and people, were overtaking Charlie all the time, usually on a corner. As one particularly reckless speedster wobbled alongside in a storm of dust and gravel I waved my fist and hurled abuse at the driver, to see, as he swerved ahead, written on a board over the back of his truck "AND THE SAME TO YOU".

So this is the great Niger river. I'm at Asaba, waiting for the ferry to Onitsha. I got here at nine this morning, and it's now noon. The string of lorries ahead of me is shorter than it was, and I have high hope of getting across on the next trip. If so, I can still reach the hospital at Ituk Mban before dusk.

Charlie attracts great interest. Maybe it's because it's the most modern vehicle in the queue by some ten or twenty years! The heat and humidity are greater than in Lagos, but seem much more tolerable here amongst the thick vegetation than in the city streets. I've made myself comfortable on the spare tyre fixed to Charlie's bonnet, looking over the noisy throng of travellers and traders. One persistent bookseller has been urging me all morning to buy a book on Advanced Physics by a Dr. Green. "You are educated," he says, "so you must read it!" When he returned for his third attempt, I had a flash of inspiration and told him "Look, I am Dr. Green! I wrote the flaming book!". He now peddles his wares at a distance, with occasional suspicious glances in my direction. His place by the Land Rover, however, has been taken by another determined pesterer, admonishing me for travelling alone. "You need servants!" he insists, and continually applies for the position. Being in this queue is like being in the stocks

- eveyone has you at their mercy, there's no escape. Another visitor is a young lad who tells me proudly he has just taken the O-Level examinations in History, having taught himself from a book he bought. He shows me his book, "1066 and All That", the splendid take-off which includes the stories of Viking Harold Harebrush, the Pheasants' Revolt and Broody Mary. I wrestle with the moral dilemma of whether to tell him that he is unlikely to have gained a pass, but thankfully, before I decide, the queue starts to move.

The ferry, a mixture of wood and metal, looks like it has been welded from an assortment of other vessels with a seasoning of modern art. Charlie follows other foolhardy travellers up an arrangement of planks. The river looks very fast and very brown and very wide. The ferry lurches violently under each addition to its load, but it must have floated to get here, and the chances are that it will make it to the other side at least once more.

The narrow road to Ituk Mban winds through villages and palm trees. I approach the hospital with mixed feelings. For one thing, Andrew and Jim and Richard are not here to see us reach our goal. For another, the hospital will be expecting a shiny new Land Rover, and Charlie is a bit bent and battered.

On Eeyore's Birthday, Pooh and Piglet brought him a pot of honey and a balloon. Before they reached Eeyore, the honey got eaten and the balloon burst, so they presented him with an empty pot and a small piece of damp material - and Eeyore was delighted! So it is with Charlie - greeted as joyfully as a "useful pot for putting things in". The hospital lorry broke down the other week, and spare parts here take a long time to arrive. Charlie's arrival, everyone says, could not have been better timed. "And what a beautiful machine!" I can feel Charlie shuffling his tyres modestly - there can be few Land Rovers with that winsome kink in the roof!

The hospital is a collection of single-storey huts with thatched roofs. Patients are fed by their families, and groups of relatives are camping outside the "wards", occasionally passing food through a window. Even the operating theatre has open windows! I ask about hygiene, and am told that since they don't have air-conditioning an open window is the only way to breathe - anyhow, there were probably fewer germs outside than in! There are plans to build a brick two-storey Nurses Home -it will be Harry's pride and joy.

Harry is a little man with a huge heart. When he arrived more than twenty years ago, he had to build a hospital from scratch. Faced with superstition, ignorance and every disease invented, he was particularly shocked by the high infant mortality rate, and decided to make maternity care his priority. He was telling me that when he first came twin babies were left in the branches of a tree - one of them had to be the devil's child, you couldn't tell which, so both had to die. Now nurses run regular prenatal and post-natal clinics throughout the area, and infant survival figures have soared.

All three of the doctors at the hospital are from Yorkshire (they explain that Methodist Missions can't be choosy!) and care for a surrounding population of a hundred and forty thousand plus. There is still plenty of illness and death around (tuberculosis is particularly widespread) but the witch-doctor has gradually been replaced by Western medicine and Christian caring.

On that first evening I was introduced to the area's staple dish, palm-oil chop. I didn't know what went into it, and was happy to leave it that way. Surely your stomach would be safe at a hospital? Anyhow, with the Expedition about over, I have become expendable. After supper we played scrabble on the verandah. Occasional shadowy figures ran through the trees in the hospital grounds, and I asked Harry what they were doing.

"Oh, it's only the Eckpo men," he explained, "a sort of secret society."

"For doing what?" I asked, in some alarm.

"I don't know. But they don't do any harm, so we ignore them. There's a lot of things we ignore, like the old German lady downriver who runs both a Mission and the local distribution network for the Fernando Po smugglers - it keeps her Mission solvent! We don't have time to do much outside the hospital - 'though sometimes you can't help getting involved in other things. I'm going down to the Calabar Law Courts tomorrow to represent the local branch of the Transport Canoe Union in a demarcation dispute."

"Why you?"

"Because they asked me to," he shrugged.

Harry's Man Friday came in to say he had "passed a bath" for me, so I went and sat in two bucketsful of tepid water and slapped at the mosquitoes attracted by the oil lamp. The hospital electricity generator was being repaired ("again" sighed Harry) else there would have been a light bulb. I didn't sleep well. It was hot and airless, and the Secret Eckpo Society was practising secret animal calls outside the window. Then just when I was dropping off, there would be the whine of a homing mosquito in one's ear. I wondered if I had remembered to take my chloroquin regularly.

Harry had left for Calabar before I woke next morning. I imparted everything I knew about Land Rovers to Okun, the hospital mechanic (who was also the hospital plumber and electrician). Then Charlie and I went over to Umahaia, the nearest town of any size, to get some supplies for the hospital. On the way we drove over a black line on the road, before realising it was a column of soldier ants on the march. Having heard of the fierce aggression of these insects, I was rather glad to be in Charlie - until a sharp stab in the nether regions caused me to stop and inspect the cause. The cause was soldier ants! They must have been thrown up by the wheels, and then had found gaps in the floor through which to attack - amazing determination! I was reminded of Tiny's words when I had asked if there were dangerous snakes or crocodiles in Eastern Nigeria, "don't worry about the animals - it's the insects you need to fear!".

That evening, the splendid group of British ladies who did many of the hospital "support" roles (nurse-training, matroning, administration, clinics, and so on) entertained me to dinner. Actually, I think that it is the ladies who form the backbone of the hospital, with the doctors providing the secondary support!

Harry was back late from Calabar, and over the "palm-oil chop" reported on the changing face of Nigerian justice, now that the wigs and robes were worn by Africans. The cases he had observed, while waiting for the Canoe Union matter to come up, included traffic violations and matrimonial disputes. One Mammy-wagon driver accused of exceeding the speed limit (and which of them didn't?) countercharged the prosecuting policeman with offering to drop the case for five shillings, and said that, in the interests of justice, he had insisted the case came to court so that he could expose this hideous corruption. The judge fined him two pounds and told him "next time, pay the policeman." The matrimonial case had been brought by a man whose wife had left him for another, and who was claiming damages from the "third party". The judge had asked him how old he was:

"Fifty, Sir."

"How old is your wife?"

"Twenty, Sir"

"And good-looking?"

"Oh, yes, very beautiful!"

"You are a very foolish old man. Case dismissed."

The consensus round the supper-table was sadness at the deterioration in the judiciary. But Harry, in his quiet and thoughtful way, wondered whether both decisions were not really quite sensible. After all, on-the-spot fines reduced the load on the courts and people marrying outside their age-group ask for trouble.

I enquired how the political system was working in the newly democratic country. "Quite well, really," one of the ladies replied. "There is what we would call Bribery and Corruption, but it's no more than the usual commercial procedure which has lubricated society here for generations. What is more serious is the racial tension between tribal groupings. The Ibo and Ibibio round here don't get on with the Yoruba from the West, and the religious differences between the Christian South and the Moslem North will also cause problems before long."

"When we British handed over," said another lady, "we suggested that our parliamentary system was jolly good, gave them a country with arbitrary boundaries and a random collection of tribes, and wished them success. We should not be too surprised, I suppose, if they go back to ways of doing things with which they are more familiar."

Today is the Fifth of November, but the fires around the village this evening are for cooking, not celebrating Guy Fawkes. The sky is overcast, for the rainy season hasn't quite finished, and the air is heavy with lurking thunder. Tomorrow Charlie's new driver will take me to Port Harcourt, whence I fly back to Lagos. I shall leave Ituk Mban with some sadness, for lovely people live here.

This morning a cyclist arrived to say that his wife had been bitten by a tree-snake a couple of days ago, and was dying. Harry was very cross, and, when I asked why, explained that the girl would probably have recovered if they could have treated her the same day. As it was, there was virtually no chance. Besides, the doctors were in the middle of operations, so there was nobody to go out to the chap's village. "Unless," he paused, "you would like to take the Land Rover and bring the patient back? Not that there's much point." But I was already seeing Charlie roaring through the bush in heroic mode, with every eye in the cinema moist, every throat complete with lump.

We threw the husband's bicycle in the back of Charlie, and set off with the husband pointing directions - having no common language would be a drawback. It was much further than I had expected. After three hours we were lurching along a narrow earthen track, when the husband pulled my sleeve and pointed at right angles to the road. I switched to four-wheel drive, took a deep breath and headed across country, hoping there were no pitfalls beneath the grass. Another few minutes and we were weaving our way along a network of rutted tracks beneath a canopy of tall trees, a bit like driving through a giant building. Every so often we passed small collections of huts that looked like decayed hayricks. This was getting a little worrying, for I had lost all sense of direction. Then, still in the gloom beneath the forest roof, we drove into another village, and my guide said something excitedly and jumped out. Evidently we had arrived.

There was a large fire burning in the centre of the settlement, and food was being prepared. There was a lot of shouting and crying going on, but I couldn't understand a word. Was the fire for a funeral pyre? Was the food for a Wake? My guide started rolling on the ground, uttering little shrieks. I stood and waited, feeling rather spare. The villagers led me to one of the huts. If only we could have spoken to each other it would have been so much better.......... It was dark inside the hut ....and smelly, and noisy. As my eyes adapted I realised there was a heap of bodies wailing on the floor. Somebody shouted something and the heap disentangled, revealing a woman's body underneath - if this was the snakebite victim, being rolled on wouldn't have helped a lot. Then I realised that everyone had formed a circle round her and me, and were waiting. They obviously thought I was a doctor.

There I am, hours from anywhere, unable to communicate and surrounded by an expectant crowd. Lonliness comes to have a new meaning. What on earth do I do?

"No, I'm not a doctor!" They nod and watch.

"I've come to take the patient in the ....ambulance." They nod again and murmur to each other, but the circle doesn't move. Why did Harry get me into this mess? I look at the curled-up little body in the gloom. Well, there's nothing else for it, I have to be the doctor. I feel for a pulse, and listen for a heartbeat, but all I can hear is my own heart thundering. What else is one supposed to do? If only I had done a first-aid course. Eyes. Yes, gently lift a lid. It doesn't look too good.. The body is very cold - well, not warm anyway. Please, God, what else can I do? Think! ..... She must be dead! There are no signs of life that I can find. I get to my feet and shake my head. For some reason this makes them much more cheerful. I've got to get out of this stifling hut!

Outside, the husband is still lying on the ground, quite silent now. I try to express my condolences - stupid phrase - by patting him on the shoulder. What a pathetic thing to do! The fire is being stoked with branches, and there's singing and chatter all around. Nobody is interested in me any more, so I return to Charlie and hope the track over there is the one we came on.

I don't remember much about the trip back, but some hours later I arrived at the hospital. Harry was scrubbing down after the operations and asked how I got on.

"I'm pretty sure she was dead," I said lamely.

"She would be," said Harry. Bless him! I felt much better.

Chapter Fourteen - Homewards

The Deputy Permanent Secretary was very apologetic. The application to waive Charlie's import duty had got lost somewhere on its tortuous journey round the warren of bureaucracy. Could I fill in another one? Yes, I could, but there were only three days before my ship sailed for England. What would happen if permission had not been obtained by then, I asked the DPS. He smiled a weary smile, and said to sit and wait a while. An hour later a perspiring clerk arrived with a letter, stamped with the seals of Customs Representative, Trade Department and Ministry of Finance. It said "I am directed to inform you that the Minister of Finance has granted your application to import a Land Rover Registered 111 JWB and engine number et cetera......" (they should have said it was known to its friends as Charlie) "....without payment of import duty, subject to the condition that the vehicle is presented as a free gift to the Ituk Mban Methodist Hospital near Uyo. You should furnish full particulars to the Chief Collector of Customs at Apapa together with the enclosed copy of this letter in order that import records may be discharged et cetera, et cetera." How on earth had the DPS managed it so quickly? I wonder if he told the Minister? Yes, of course he did - he's British, so wouldn't dream of bending the rules. Would he?

I suddenly realised that I wasn't particularly elated by the news, any more than I had been angry that the original application had been lost. Both events were just noted - with interest, but at a distance. It was as if one's emotional circuits had burnt out and events were registered impassively - it was just too much trouble to cry or laugh any more. Is that what Africa does to you? You start out protesting about incompetence and fretting over delay, and you end up meekly accepting things, assuming that everything will get sorted out eventually. And then I wondered what on earth I would have done if permission hadn't been granted?

I wrote a quick note to Harry, to let him know the hospital wouldn't get a bill and imagined his quiet smile as he strummed his guitar in the candlelight. I feel guilty in a way to be going home and leaving him behind, for I know how much he misses his wife and family in Ilkley.

I came back from Eastern Nigeria a couple of days ago. The flight to Lagos from Port Harcourt was grim with a capital grrr. It started well enough, the Fokker Friendship taking off smoothly from the landing strip between the palm trees, and flying over the swampy forest coast. Below, the network of creeks weaving their tangled web looked quite photogenic in the setting sun. Not that I really appreciated the sight, for I had had a violent headache for two days and was convinced that it must be Blackwater Fever or something equally terminal. I remember thinking that somewhere down below, where little green treesnakes patrolled the canopy, there would be other headaches after a village funeral wake.

Then the waiting thunderstorm struck. I wondered if it was the same one that had battered Charlie a week before on the way out - miffed at losing its prey and now bent on vengeance. The 'plane window was alternately black as black and then lit with dazzling electric brilliance. I just hoped the Nigerian pilots knew what they were doing. I would have felt happier with Brits at the controls! The 'plane was imitating an express elevator in the violent air-currents, shooting up and down and sometimes seemingly both together, wings flapping like an arthritic goose and the passengers shouting and squealing. Not that I shouted and squealed - good gracious, no! It was not so much British stoicism, more like rigid terror. As I gripped the jolting seat in front and tried to keep up with my stomach, the fact that I was suffering from acute pestilence didn't seem all that important any more. The flight was like the worst Irish Sea crossings, when you are torn between fear that the end is nigh, and fear that it's not.

Anyhow that was ages ago, two days at least. The next day my headache had gone, so it probably wasn't Blackwater Fever after all. Instead of dying, I went to the Ministry of Finance, like I told you. And then on to the Chief Collector of Customs at steamy Apapa Wharf. He read the letter with all the seals on it, but the procedure for waiving duty seemed new to him. He asked where the Land Rover was, and I said Eastern Nigeria, and he said "Ah!" knowingly, frowned at the ceiling and looked out of the window. He read the letter again. The bit about "discharging import records" was clearly a worry. Time was getting on, so I suggested he stamp the letter (and

Charlie's log book, and the AA carnet, and the insurance certificate, and anything else that came to hand) with his seal, and the records would then probably be well and truly discharged. He agreed, and I had time to pick up the mail back in central Lagos before the bank closed. Charlie's "clearance papers" from the South African agents had arrived, a mere two weeks too late. There was also a letter from my dear niece, reminding me that she had only *lent* me Tigger. I hoped she would like his flatter shape and the subtle scent of Damascus drainage.

Back at the Regent Hotel, the other guests told me I'd missed all the excitement. Evidently there had been a demonstration against something or other, and any vehicle driven by a White had been stoned as it ran the gauntlet across the bridge to the business centre. One poor American lady had stalled her car in the middle of the bombardment and things had looked rather nasty, but then the hail of stones stopped, and the crowd ran to help push. Once the engine started they rushed back for more stones to fling at its departing rear. It was clearly unsporting to stone a sitting target - what a testimony to British influence!

Sitting across the room at dinner was an old man noisily sucking up soup. He had long untidy hair and wore a jacket several sizes too large. I wondered if he was a dispossessed Hungarian refugee - it was either that or an itinerant Australian musician. To my surprise he came over after the meal, saying he had heard I was from Cambridge. He had been there in the Twenties, and now ran a Lancashire engineering company which was tendering for a project in Lagos. We talked a long time - about universities and schools, the relative merits of breadth and depth in education, teaching machines, and goodness knows what else. He reminded me of Uncle Phil - always asking my opinion on things about which he was more knowledgeable. I felt rather ashamed of myself for judging people on appearance.

It was getting late and I was about to yawn and retire, when he asked me how I rated the chances of democracy continuing in Africa. Now, this was something on which I regarded myself as a bit of an expert, having been in Africa for ten weeks. The poor chap must have been bored silly as I informed him that the chances of success must be predicated on the fact that power in African society traditionally lay with a system of paramount chiefs, unused to letting committees make decisions and even less used to voluntarily giving someone else a turn at governing. No, said I, it would be generations before power genuinely lay with the people in the established British way. He asked how long power in Britain had been determined democratically - by a majority of the people including women. I dredged my recollection of history lessons, and said probably less than fifty years. He just smiled.

"Ah, yes," I blustered, "but before the verdict of the ballot box is respected there needs to be an established system of law and order! Here in Africa order is fragile, and law is reverting to the whim of those in power. The new African politicians are so.... so self-seeking."

"And politicians in our country aren't?"

A lot later I think we concluded that it was not possible to have both freedom and democracy. It was something to do with freedom requiring strong government, which democracy, inhibited by the need for short-term popularity, was unable to produce. I forget the details, but it sounded good at the time.

It's the evening of Tuesday, November 10th. and the TSMV "Accra" is about to leave. This morning I did the goodbyes: a courtesy call at the UNESCO office and a visit to thank Tiny. Then I packed my bag, settled my hotel bill, and hailed a taxi. Two drivers pulled up, so I asked each how much the fare was to the Elder-Dempster stores. One said fifteen shillings, the other said ten and won the honour. But when we arrived, he had changed his mind and said the charge was a pound. I gave him ten shillings. The situation then escalated when he refused to give me my bag. I looked around for some authority figure to whom I could appeal, but the street seemed empty. Well, on my last day here I was not going to be defeated by African duplicity, and I was bigger than he was, so I took the ignition-keys from the car, which I offered to exchange for my luggage. It seemed fair to me, but he got very annoyed and produced a knife. This was getting unpleasant, and I remember thinking how stupid it would be to get killed now, after surviving so long! But rational thought had gone. The contest was between right and wrong, and in such a noble cause one must be prepared to suffer. I'm surprised I didn't sing Land of Hope and Glory.

We circled with the car between us. It seemed that a gesture of compromise was urgently required, so I threw his keys as far as I could. He raced to get them. I picked up my bag and hared for the warehouse. The bag was heavy, and I could hear feet behind gaining fast before I was halfway to the door. I was gasping for breath and awaiting a nasty sensation between the shoulder blades, when a nasal Merseyside voice said "Having trouble, mate?" Never can a group of Liverpool sailors have been more welcome. The taxi driver stopped, made a snarling sound, and went back to his car, leaving me to thank the rescue squad!

The rest of the day has been less exciting. I collected my sheaves of questionnaires and two smelly Basuto sheepskins from storage, and the Liverpudlian support group took me and my luggage through the customs sheds to the ship. The only hitch was currency control. I had drawn the Expedition's remaining funds from the bank to take back to England, and I dutifully filled in the declaration forms.

"You have declared ninety pounds sterling!"

"Yes."

"You are only allowed to take out fifty pounds."

"The bank never mentioned that."

"It is none of the bank's business. Customs decides how much you are allowed. We don't have to tell anybody what we are doing."

"Wouldn't it help if you did - before people have money transferred out here?"

"We set the rules. They are there to be obeyed!" I could feel my colonial hackles rising - I was no longer the nice polite boy who had left Dover in July.

"I have travelled through dozens of African countries," I said with what I intended to be icy dignity with a touch of steel at the edges, "and I've never come across anything so ridiculous! I am a personal friend of your Finance Minister, and I shall have to take this up with him!" I was waved through with no further delay. May my arrogance and untruthfulness be forgiven. No wonder the world is so full of cads and bounders, when caddery and bounding is so frequently rewarded.

The Accra's engines are throbbing now, and we start to edge out from the wharf and down the channel. Leaning on the rail, looking down on Africa sliding away, it feels good. I am no longer vulnerable, no longer subject to arbitrary decisions. I start to relax for the first time in ages. We come round a promontory where a military guard is drawn up. As we pass, the parade comes to attention and a bugle sounds out over the water. I wonder what that is about, and then I see a British officer in dress uniform standing on the upper deck, rigidly to attention, hand vibrating in salute, tears pouring down his face and dripping off the quivering white moustache. Not everyone is happy to be going back to England.

A single blast of the ship's horn signals noon. We've churned steadily West for four days, stopping briefly at Takoradi in Ghana, and then at Freetown, Sierra Leone. The "Accra" is not in the same league as the Mokoto - for one thing, passengers are discouraged from mixing with the crew, and instead have to endure each other's company. A boring lot they are. I'm quite sure they include no female between the age of ten and thirty. I sit at a table with a family of very Methodist missionaries returning on leave - pleasant enough, but lacking sparkle, if you know what I mean. I try to introduce a challenging topic of conversation each day, to brighten up mealtimes, but they refuse to rise to the bait and just go quiet. You could almost imagine they dislike me! Still, I suppose one can't expect all missionaries to be up to the Ituk Mban standard.

The ship does its best to organise diversions. We have chess competitions, a daily news-sheet and crossword, hearty gallumphing around in sports competitions and treasure-hunts. Oh yes, and the daily mileage sweepstakes (there is no independent means of verifying the result, and I think the winner is fixed!) - my plan for tomorrow is to bribe the First Officer to announce that the lucky winner of the day's lottery is the Methodist missionary. Maybe I'd better not, since the ship's doctor is ill at the moment. The food, at least, is very good - masses of fresh fruit, so there's little chance of scurvy.

Idleness is bliss for only a day or two, so now I'm sorting out the responses on our teachers' questionnaires. I've set myself a modest five hours a day target - the brain has become unused to office discipline, but it would be nice to finish the report before reaching England. Educational surveys tend to be dull, and therefore ignored, so I must start by grabbing the attention.

"In Africa the need for education is as great as the teachers are few." A pithy statement of the problem, but perhaps a bit over-simplified? Will it rivet the mind? Does it kindle the desire to read on? Maybe not. I'll try another opening. We are now following the African coast as it turns North. A gentle swell disturbs the sunlight into patterns on the surface. The temperature is 85 degrees F., but the sea breeze makes it very acceptable.

"The purpose of this survey is to identify the obstacles that self-teaching techniques might encounter in Africa." A bit negative perhaps. And should it be "might" or "may"? The first sentence occupies all morning.

Flying fish in ones and twos skim away from our bows, airborne for a hundred yards at a time. A school of porpoise wheels dorsal fins through the surface alongside us, like some sea-monster of old. Now and then fat grey-turquoise bodies break free and arc sleekly through the air.

"The European child grows up surrounded by the mechanical and electrical manifestations of a prosperous technological civilisation. The African child grows up in an agricultural society, the family housed in a small room or hut. There are few books and most children have never seen ships or the sea, office blocks or films. They may not be able to change a light bulb because electricity is new to them, but there is no evidence that African races are less 'intelligent' than Caucasian races." Anyone can forget to put oil in the engine of the Customs' launch if he is experienced only with bicycles. A fishing boat, rusty white, is signalling to us, and we slow down alongside. It has run out of fresh water, and a few buckets of our plenty are roped down.

The Basuto sheep-skins come in handy for the Fancy Dress Competition. They still have a rather strong odour, but I am an Ancient Briton, and Ancient Britons probably didn't smell too good. Nor were they necessarily thick because they couldn't change light bulbs. The chief steward is one of the judges, and I find that he comes from Colby, just a few miles from my home. Huge triumph - Ancient Briton gets First Prize! On merit, of course.

Las Palmas was just another port. I didn't bother going ashore - too hot and tiring. "With a tradition of repetitive verbal learning,

African students rely heavily on memory of the words, rather than understanding of the concepts. The teaching of science in particular requires careful demonstrations." Cape St. Vincent is outlined in the cold mist off the Starboard bow (note the nice turn of nautical phrasing). If Browning's epic had it nobly, nobly disappearing to the West he must have been heading for the Mediterranean.

I reach "Conclusions" on page twenty-nine. We are coming to the hardest part. To summarise by saying "there is a shortage of pencils and food" may be true but doesn't justify the previous twenty-eight pages. Besides, UNESCO wants solutions to problems, which is why self-teaching programmes are being promoted. So maybe I should say that self-teaching programmes work, which is true, but that even the cheapest form of booklet will cost more to produce than can be afforded. That's not very constructive. What ways can we develop to use self-teaching less expensively?

Cape Finisterre (I've just realised it means "land's end") lies to the East across the grey wind-whipped sea. Browning probably couldn't think of anything to rhyme with it, which is doubtless why there's no epic Finisterre poem. We left Nigeria over a week ago, and now it's hard to remember what it felt like to be too hot. If only one could mix a little of Lagos with the Bay of Biscay, both might be improved.

Now for the crisp incisive Summary. "Perhaps the value of Programmed Instruction lies in illustrating the core mechanics of human learning. Producing Programmes will teach teachers how to teach. If they teach more efficiently as a result. we have made a significant contribution to African Education." Do I believe that? The Bay of Biscay isn't as rough as I had expected.

The Mersey Pilot came aboard at Holyhead. The low drizzle-clouds hide the Welsh mountains. I have dreamed of English Autumn days - the taste of blackberries, the smell of garden bonfires, Jim and Andrew presiding over Hollantide Fayres on vicarage lawns, and gentle evenings tinged with wistfulness. And what do we have? Drizzle. Maybe there's always drizzle in Liverpool.

I just don't see how anything can help Africa at the moment. Worse still, I don't think Africa deserves helping. But I musn't say that

- I can't support such a statement objectively and it sounds like juvenile petulance. OK, OK. Final paragraph ....heading Recommendations ....I wonder if anyone will read it?

It's funny being home. The period spent in Africa was a lifetime, yet now those five months have somehow been erased, like a wound closing. Except that the simile is misleading, for you don't want to re-open a wound, but already I want to go back to Africa. Besides, it can't have been worse than Sheffield in Winter.

A letter has just come from Harry. Charlie is doing splendidly - "transporting fuel and corpses".

Footnote:
Andrew became a vicar in York, then in Devon..
David became a Member of the Manx parliament.
Jim became Bishop of Bath and Wells.
Richard spent a lifetime in Africa, latterly at the University of Namibia.

Epilogue

The two men seem neither young nor old. They talk enthusiastically, but move a bit stiffly. From their relaxed laughter it appears they know each other well.

"Was it really forty years ago?" the tall vicar is saying.

"Remind me why we went," says the lecturer from Namibia.

"It was what people did before backpacking, wasn't it?"

"Yes, but we went for a reason! Teaching machines wasn't it?"

"Which reminds me, what became of the Report and Recommendations to UNESCO?" asks the vicar, polishing his glasses.

"As I understand it, they sent a letter of acknowledgement, and that was it. Nothing further was heard. But shortly afterwards they seemed to lose interest in educating Africa by self-teaching booklets. A pity really. I still think the idea had possibilities." He sighs.

"So, what did we achieve?" There is a pause.

"Well, we got a Land Rover to a hospital."

"Yes, what happened to Charlie?"

"Requisitioned by the Biafran army. Exit, pursued by bullets."

"What a shame! Poor old thing!" The vicar shakes his head. "So our survey wasn't used, and the Land Rover was stolen?"

"Come on, that's being a bit negative. I think that the whole thing was very worthwhile! By the way, did you get a copy of the 'To Travel Hopefully' book? I thought it was quite good."

"He can use that rave review on the back cover!"

"It won't sell, though - no sex or violence!"